Michael Kerr was born and grew up in Northern Ireland and now lives near London, where he has been a journalist since 1977. This is his first book.

Our Side of the House

Michael Kerr

Quartet Books

First published in 2002 by Quartet Books Ltd
A member of the Namara Group
27 Goodge Street London W1P 2LD

A catalogue record for this book is available from the
British Library

ISBN 0 7043 8163 X

Phototypeset by FiSH Books, London WC1
Printed and bound by CPD, Wales

For my family

Acknowledgements

Acknowledgement is made to the following for permission to quote from copyright works: Laurence Pollinger Ltd and the Estate of Frieda Lawrence Ravagli for lines from *Sons and Lovers* by D. H. Lawrence; International Music Publications Ltd for lines from 'Child of the Universe' by John Lees, © 1975 RAK Publishing Ltd, London NW8 7BU.

This book could not have been written without the help and patience of my family in England, Ireland and Australia. I am indebted to all of them, but especially to Teri, who put up with the silent Saturdays and the endless revisions.

Thanks are also due to: Jeremy Beale, Graham Boynton, Cherie Burns, Esmond Harmsworth and Judith Woods.

One

If it had been a woman I wouldn't have minded so much. If it had been a good-looking one I'd have been tempted to slip in beside her. But I nearly got under the covers with some oul' baldie.

'Ah'm sorry, darlin', but ye know how it is,' my Ma said. And I do. I know that when you live in a boarding house you live an insecure life. One minute you have a room; next minute you've been kicked out of it to make way for a paying customer, somebody who's turned up in Portstewart as carelessly as Mary and Joseph did in Bethlehem. The difference, of course, is that we don't turn them away, these waifs and strays, these hard-luck cases who've been lucky enough to bump into my Da as he sinks his fifth or sixth Bush in the Sea Splash. We put ourselves out for them, literally. 'Yer house is never yer own,' my Ma will eventually say when somebody asks her about the downside of the catering business. Your house? Never mind your house. It's your bloody bed you can't count on.

Why tonight of all nights? Is it too much to ask, when you've walked all the way from Portrush in new platform shoes, to be allowed to collapse into your own pit? The sound of those shoes hitting the kitchen tiles was the best thing I've heard all night. Better than 'Dancing Queen', better than 'Brown Sugar', better than 'Drift Away'. Better even than the noise that wee girl made when she was blowing in my ear during the first slow one. And that came to nothing anyway.

It's a wonder I've any toes left. Dick and Aidan thought it was hilarious: 'Look at the shape o' him – totterin' about like a tart in stilettos.' All my own bloody fault, first for not breaking them in and then for insisting on that last round. If I hadn't done that I could have bought us a taxi home.

So much for not drinking. So much for the deal I made with my Ma. She pays for *NME* and *Sounds* and *Melody Maker* every week and in return I promise not to follow my Da, not to drink every penny she earns.

I kept to it for a long time. I did everything a Pioneer does except wear the pin. 'Come on, Mick, have a pint,' the other guys used to say. 'Your Ma's not here, and *we're* not gonna tell her.' But I didn't. Not till that night at Kelly's when I thought I'd found the woman of my dreams, and she asked me to buy her a beer and then said she was going to the loo and would be back in two ticks . . . It would have been a shame to waste it.

I didn't waste any of it tonight. I've put away far too much. But then I was the one having the final fling before going away to college. Aidan didn't have that excuse. He'd have taken a pop at Johnny Thompson on the way out if I hadn't hustled him past. Johnny looked at me as if to say, 'You've got some nice friends.' I suppose in Aidan's eyes he was a pushover. He is tiny. In his bow tie and white shirt, next to the rest of the gorillas, he looks more like a waiter than a bouncer. Only the nose gives him away.

Aidan was all for going back when I'd wrestled him out to the car park. 'Who is that wee shit, anyway?'

He didn't believe me when I told him. Neither did Dick. 'An Olympic boxer? You're kiddin'? And Elizabeth's his girlfriend? Lucky bastard. She's fuckin' gorgeous.'

Yeah, I've seen how Dick looks at her when he comes round, and he can't understand why I don't feel the same way. But Elizabeth's not just some cute bank clerk who happens to be living under our roof; she's been here so long she seems like a sister. I'd no more want to go to bed with her than I would with Maisie. God, what a horrible thought! A nurse'd be nice. But not a nurse who flashes blue veins when she's settling herself on the settee.

Dick was still dribbling on about Elizabeth when we got out on the road. Then he moved on to the bite on his neck and just how he got it. Aidan didn't say a bloody word all the way into Portrush, so I thought tonight the RUC might be safe from even non-verbal communication. But they weren't – as he turned away from the two of us and went past the barracks he gave them the fingers as usual, and then we got the thumbs up. 'See ya tomorrow, you guys.'

We'd nearly passed Judette's old house when Dick grabbed me by the arm. 'Mick, doesn't your sister live somewhere round here? Remember the night we woke them up? Ah'm glad it's not like that tonight.'

So was I. It was so bloody wet that night we could nearly have swum along the road. Even so, I wouldn't have stopped if I hadn't seen a light on. And once we *had* stopped, Judette wouldn't let us walk on.

'Ye will *not*,' she said, looking at me as if I was still the wee brother who woke screaming in the night, the one whose nightmares she cuddled away. Her first idea was that we should all sleep on the floor. But that wouldn't do. If my Ma woke and I wasn't in the house she'd be frantic, and we couldn't phone her at this time. It wouldn't be fair; nobody needs her sleep more than my Ma. 'Right, there's nothin' else for it – Derek'll have tae run ye home.'

So Derek, the poor bugger, having gone to bed after a couple of pints, got turfed out of it to cram us all in the MG. Knowing the way he feels about drink-driving, I bet he was cursing me up and down. 'No problem,' he said when he dropped me at the front door, but I knew that for once he didn't mean it.

At least he's not going to get caught like that again – even if he had to take Judette as far as Australia to make absolutely certain. Judette, Roisin, Trish and Bredge: half the family on the other side of the world. 'Ah hate tae see them go,' my Ma says, 'but sure what is there tae keep them here?'

'And you'll be off soon, too,' she said the other night, giving me a pretend box on the ear, as if leaving home was like eating the last of the Jammy Dodgers she'd been saving for the visitors. 'But at least you're only going tae London...'

She knows I could be staying even nearer home, but I think she understands why I'm not. 'You could study journalism in Belfast and get a job there,' that guy said to me at the interview. 'I could,' I told him. 'But I'm not going to. Because I don't want to work on a sectarian rag, and I don't want aldermen and councillors, when I'm noting down their circumlocutions, to be asking themselves whether I'm a Catholic journalist or a Protestant one.'

I've got it well rehearsed now, just as I'll have *Lun–dun* well rehearsed by the time I get there. Bye-bye, *Lunt'n*, hello *Lun–dun*. My mouth widens when I say it in front of the mirror, so you can see more of my teeth. My Irish picket-fence teeth, ruined by Highland Toffee and Ernest Walmsley. 'Right, son, open wide. Good. All looks fine to me.' Well, it didn't look fine to me. I could see my mouth was too crowded. But you can't say that when you're a wee boy and the dentist knows better, can you? Even if I wasn't as wee as he seemed to think. There I was, nine or ten, and he was still saying to me, 'Well, son, and what's Santy Claus bringing you this Christmas?' More sweets, probably, as if I needed any. It's not all his fault my teeth are rotten. If I'd stayed out of Scilleys' and Herbisons' and left the toffee and the clove rock alone, I wouldn't be afraid to smile. I can say *Lunt'n* and hardly show the teeth. But *Lun–dun*'s, different, *Lun–dun*'s toothier. It makes me sound like a BBC Northern Ireland news-reader. Like W. D. Flackes. Like a Protestant.

It doesn't suit me; it doesn't fit me any better than those bloody shoes. I'm not taking them to London. I'll give them to Sean. Sean'll be glad of them.

I could have sworn it was him I heard snoring when I

went up the stairs. My Da's a coffee percolator, Sean's a whiffler. In with a deep breath, then out with wee puffs that set his lips trembling. I'm amazed he's never tickled himself awake. But then you could run a train under his bed in the middle of the night and he wouldn't hear it. Soon as his head hits the pillow that's it until – I don't know – early afternoon, anyway, when Peter O'Doherty and your man Hayes call for him to go round to the Splash. 'I'm a joiner,' he says, 'but there's no work round here for joiners, so I just join the rest o' them in the pub.' I can't blame him. Not even when he comes home pissed and blunders around in the dark like a mummy shedding bandages; he only does it because he thinks that if he turned on the light he'd wake me up. If I hadn't made a point of returning the compliment I'd have noticed a damn sight sooner that it wasn't him in the bed.

Just as well that whoever he is is a snorer. There I am with one foot on, ready to spring over to the far side, when he starts whiffling again, and I'm thinking, Sean, if you're going to be doing that all night, I want you whiffling at the wall and not at the back of my neck. So I give him a nudge, and out comes that head. Hairless as an egg.

If my Ma didn't hear me going up the stairs, she damn well heard me on the way back down. She was already pushing herself up on the pillows when I stepped over the threshold.

'Have you been drinkin'?'

'Ah have not.'

'Well, ye don't seem too steady on yer pins.'

'Ah'm just tired. Ah had tae walk all the way home.'

'Ye did what?'

'Shush. Ye'll wake mae Da. It's only three and a bit miles. An' it's a nice walk. Even the caravans at Juniper Hill look pretty on a night like this.'

She's always telling me it's caravans that have ruined the boarding houses of Northern Ireland. Sometimes I think she feels they've done more damage than the bombers.

'Huh. You shoulda been in yer bed hours ago.'

I told her it was just as well I hadn't been, seeing as Theo Kojak was in it already.

That softened her. 'Och, Michael, darlin'. Didn't ye see the note? Ah left ye a note in the kitchen. That fella's from Tyrone, some relation o' yer Daddy's. He turned up wi' nowhere tae stay at half eleven.'

So I reminded her that all my stuff for college is in that room, including the new tape recorder I've bought so I can be a proper journalist.

'It'll be all right. He'll not touch it. Now, go on tae bed.'

'Where?'

'In the breakfast room. I've put you and Sean down a mattress in there.'

In the breakfast room. Of course. Where else would a fella sleep? And why do we call it the breakfast room when it's the living room? It's not as if any of us ever eats breakfast in it. Only Maisie and Elizabeth do that, and they have their dinner and tea in there, too. Except in the summer, of course, when the breakfast room is being used as a bedroom and they have to have all their meals in the dining room. Where, of course, we never dine ourselves. And, except at Christmas and on a few odd Sundays when the house is nearly empty, we never sit in

7

the sitting room. We don't even think of it as our sitting room. It's *their* sitting room, the visitors' sitting room.

Visitors, that's a laugh. Everybody else has visitors who pop round for a couple of hours and have a cup of tea and a biscuit and a chinwag over the price of spuds and their slipped disc and then go home. But our visitors arrive for dinner and they're still here for breakfast. And they stay for weeks or months or, if they're like Maisie, for bloody ever.

'You'll be glad to get away from Northern Ireland,' that guy said at the interview. And I will – but not only for the reasons he had in mind. It'll be good to have a room in a hall of residence that's been let to me and can't be sublet to anybody else. Then when I come back in the evening I can step into bed without having to check that there isn't some bald stranger in it already.

'Ye get used tae anythin',' my Ma's always saying, but I've still not got used to that, and I've had plenty of time. Sure it's been going on since I was four years old.

I don't remember there being any visitors in Heathmount. Just Mrs O'Donnell tickling my face with her white whiskers and all those rides I used to get on Rosaleen McCracken's dog, as if I was a cowboy on the prairie instead of a wean in the front room. But I know we didn't have a sign saying 'Board Residence'. That didn't go up until we moved in here, some time in '62.

Sean would have been whiffling in his cot then, but softer than he's doing now. Better just check it *is* him in the breakfast room.

My Da's plastered and skimmed and stripped and papered and painted every inch of the house over the years, but this door's one of those things he's never got round to fixing. All it needs is a bit of paint planed off the edge, but it's never happened. You push it. It sticks. So you push it again. And it swings, juddering, into the room, with that wee brass ring round the handle jangling, just as it's doing now.

And that definitely *is* Sean. Nobody else has hair that frizzy apart from Uncle Josey. But he doesn't look like Josey at the minute. The moustache he's trying to grow, combined with the hair, makes him look more like one of those guys who sing the *doo-wops* in a soul band. At least it would do if he had a tan, but, as I keep telling him, he's never going to get one of those if he spends the rest of his days propping up the bar in the Sea Splash.

Why does he have to lie diagonally? He's left me no room at all. Should I push him over a bit now? No point. By the time I've had a cup of tea he'll have rolled back anyway. Leave him where he is for the moment.

Fuck, these tiles are cold! Mind you, I'd sooner be barefoot than wearing those shoes.

At least the big kettle's still warm; a couple of minutes on the gas and it should be boiling. That's assuming I can ever get the gas lit. I hate these lighters. 'Press button,' it says. 'When wire glows, hold over gas.' Except the wire never bloody glows; not for me, anyway. Did I see my Ma put matches in the pull-down cupboard earlier?

I did. The Pull-Down Cupboard – so called to distinguish it from The Cupboard, which has drawers and doors but not a flap that pulls down; a flap where my Ma leans to scribble her shopping lists and make her entries in the big red Nestlé Catering Service Bookings book: '17 July to 24 July, the Murphys and three sons in the

Back Return; 24 July to 31 July, Mr and Mrs Hawke from Hamilton, Lanarkshire, Scotland, in Miss Lambert's Room...'

The Back Return. Miss Lambert's Room. The Big Front Attic. The Back House. 'I could write a book,' my Ma's always saying. 'There's a story for every room in the house.' And there is, too. If I was doing it, I think I'd start with the scullery.

Two

Scullery. The word makes me think of a maid, which is what my Ma was when she first came to Portstewart. A maid in marital status and by occupation. I love that story of hers about the oul' targe she worked for in the house beside the York Hotel.

There's my Ma scrubbing off the grime after a hard day's work when there's a knock on the bathroom door. She wraps herself in a towel and opens the door.

'Miss Cassidy,' says the oul' targe, 'what do you think you are doing?'

My Ma gives her the blindingly obvious answer, but politely.

'Well,' says the oul' targe, 'I'll have you know, Miss Cassidy, that the bathroom in this house is solely for my use. I do not wish to see you in it again. *Ever.* Do I make myself clear?'

She does. So the following day my Ma hops over the fence and finds herself a job with the people next door. And while she's out at the front one day, shining the windows with a newspaper, that young plasterer Mick Kerr cycles past and whistles at her legs. They court (chastely, of course), marry, and go off for a few days' honeymoon to Bundoran where, as they walk arm in arm on the beach, they're accosted by the now notorious traveller woman. My Da buys a sprig of her heather, but she's not content with that. She tells him he's mean and should buy the whole bunch. He dips in his pocket for a few bob more, but my Ma, minding the pennies even on her honeymoon, puts her hand on his arm. 'No, Mick,' she says. 'Don't buy them for me. Ah don't want them.' So my Da tells the traveller woman to piss off and leave them alone. And she does. But as she reaches the top of a sand dune she turns and bellows: 'I know the pair of ye's just married, and let me tell ye this: Ye'll never see the face o' yer own child.'

That must have scared the shit out of them. Bound to have. My Ma makes light of it now, but you can tell it put the wind up her. Or it would have done if she hadn't had a hotline to St Jude, the Patron Saint of Hopeless Cases. Look at us now. There's a roll-call of Kerrs that would keep a village school going:

Judette
Roisin
Anne
Patricia
Bredge
Me

Sean
Danny
and Peter.

We must have been here a year before Danny arrived, and Peter was two years after that, so neither of them will remember how small the scullery used to be. You could put a double mattress down on the floor now and have room to walk all the way round it. You could, but we haven't. It's possibly the only room in the house that hasn't been slept in by somebody at some stage. I wonder why...

Kettle's boiling. Up it comes and − yes − another lovely shower of sparks from its black bottom, like the briefest of shooting stars. There'd be none of those if it was used only on the gas, if it didn't sit for so long on the range having its bottom warmed by coal. Might as well make a pot; I don't feel like sleeping yet. A dribble to warm the pot, a swirl around, and then a couple of spoonfuls of Stewarts'. 'I can't stan' the taste o' that oul' Typhoo, and them bags are worse,' my Ma says. But I'd never let it stew the way she does; I don't want a mug of tar.

I'd have been sucking my tea from a plastic beaker when we moved in, dribbling it all over the floor as I followed my Ma everywhere, even into spaces like the scullery where there was only room for one. I was squeezing in next to her that day when I nudged against the spuds in their hessian bag. The spuds nudged me back. I yelped. The spuds started to dance. I screamed the house down. That was the last I saw of the turkey until it was in bits under the bread sauce.

I think it was that same Christmas Davy Murray bought me the cowboy and Indian. Could they really have been a foot tall? I know they seemed like it. I made them fight all day, and the cowboy won every time because the Indians were always baddies. It said so on the television.

'Where do all the dead Indians go, Mammy?'

'I sweep them out from the back o' the television every mornin', son. Great big heaps o' them.'

Davy was a sweeper, too, when he wasn't a labourer, and it was from him that I first heard that song:

> *My old man's a dustman,*
> *He wears a dustman's hat.*
> *He wears oul' baggy trousers*
> *An' he lives in a council flat.*

But Davy didn't live in a council flat; he lived in our house. His sister had had a row with him and thrown him out and my Ma could never understand why. 'He's no trouble,' she'd say. 'Ye'd never know he's in the house.'

Yeah. Sure. I remember them waking us – him and my Da – when they came home full some nights. My Ma would try to shush them in the hall.

'Where have you pair o' boys been till this time?'

'We had a few wee jobs tae do,' my Da would tell her.

'Huh. Ah know rightly what sort o' wee jobs ye've been doin'.'

Then the singing would start. '*Come by the hills to the land where –* '

'Will ye pipe down before ye wake the whole house.'

A scuffle. Giggles. My Ma squealing, 'Oh, don't tickle me. *Doh*–ant!'

Then the kitchen door would close, there'd be a tapping on the tiles, and I'd know my Da and Davy were trying to get my Ma to dance. Where my feet are stretched out now: that's where they would have been whirling and twirling her, two guilty men trying, and succeeding, to spin her anger into laughter.

'Will ye catch yersels on?' I'd hear her say. 'Ye'll not be nearly as bright the morra when there's work tae be done.'

There was plenty of that. 'Built by fishermen, rebuilt by Mick Kerr,' my Da used to say. If he's right, the whole terrace went up around the 1800s to keep fishermen busy during a poor season. From the sound of things not much had been done to this place between then and the day we arrived – apart from the painting those soldiers gave it when they had it as a billet. Everything in muddy military brown. 'Doors, cupboards, architraves, skirtin' board. It's a bloomin' wonder they didn't put it on the curtains as well,' my Da says. By all accounts, it was the paint that was holding the place together. Nothing else was sound. The floors were springing up and the ceilings falling down. Roisin's never done telling me that I wouldn't be here at all if she hadn't snatched me out of bed that night when the plaster started to bury me. 'An' ye slept right through the whole thing' – just like Sean's doing now in the breakfast room.

I wonder if he remembers much of those times – my Da working night and day on the house with Davy lending a hand now and again. I thought my Da was a superman. Shame it couldn't have stayed like that. On our walks to the shops and the chapel my Ma gave me the idea that he'd built half the town.

'It was yer father and Bertie Boyd built that house...

'...Ye should see the front room in there – yer Daddy made a quare job o' the ceilin'...

'...That was a throughother place till yer Daddy got started on it.'

And now he was sorting out our own house. When the girls were at school and Sean was asleep or in his high-chair in the kitchen, I'd race up the stairs and watch him plastering the walls. He worked fast, always with a cigarette in his mouth which jiggled up and down whenever he was answering my questions.

'What's that big square thing, Daddy?'

'That's the hawk.'

'Why's it called a hawk?'

'Ah couldn't tell ye, son. That's just what we've always called it. But it's the greatest thing in the world for carryin' plaster. See...ye put the plaster on here from the bucket and then ye can take it roun' the room.'

'An' what's that ye've got in yer han' now?'

'That's the float. That's for smoothin' it out. You watch this...'

He moved the float in a swift arc over the wall and every bump and ridge disappeared.

'Feel that – gently now, wi' the palm o' yer han'.'

I touched the wall. It felt lovely.

'D'ye think yer Mammy'll be happy wi' that?'

'Aye, Ah'm sure she will. Will Ah get her tae come and have a look?'

'Naw, it's a bit early tae be doin' that. But ye could go down and tell her this plasterer she's taken on is gettin' tired. He wants tae know if he's allowed a tea break. An' when ye get down there see if there's any sign o' Davy

16

Murray. He promised tae give me a hand as soon as he got home . . . An' don't be runnin'. . .'

But I was already halfway down.

I was easily pleased in those days. The highlight of the afternoon came when Davy arrived home, opened his piece box and held up the Penguin or the Wagon Wheel he'd saved to split between Bredge and me. Sometimes, if my Da had been out building the town, both he and Davy would come home with something saved, so there'd be a biscuit each and no need to share. And sometimes Davy came home after a really long day and had eaten the biscuit himself, so there was no handout at all. But I didn't love him any less.

I loved him even that one morning he seriously let me down.

There I was, the family bed-wetter, and I'd done it one more time.

'Och, Michael, not again,' my Ma said, pulling back the bedclothes, catching me before I could get out of bed and pin the blame on Sean. 'Do ye not think Ah've got enough washin' to do? WheninunderGod are ye goin' tae stop? Come on – get outta there till I get this sheet off and get it in the sink.'

And I got out with my head lowered, avoiding her eye, while she grabbed the sheet and jerked it free and revealed that patch of red rubber covering the mattress on my side. That was there, I knew, because my Ma couldn't trust me.

Funny I should be remembering all this as I stand pouring another cup of tea. I hope by this stage I really am past wetting my bed . . .

I'd lie awake for ages in those days trying to prevent

the inevitable, praying to the baby Jesus and Mary and Joseph and St Jude for help. Or I'd wake in the middle of the night, and be so pleased to find I was still dry, and creep to the toilet to make sure I stayed that way. My Ma often heard me. 'Are ye goin' tae the toilet? Good boy.' No matter how long I stood over the bowl there was never more than a dribble, but I could picture the flood that would come later. How come Sean was two years younger and he had no trouble controlling his bladder? Why did I have to be alone in my shame?

Then Davy came down that morning, minutes after my Ma had rinsed the sheet, and announced: 'Mrs Kerr, my bed's wet – '

'Och, Davy, surely not,' she said with a smile. 'Never mind. It could happen tae anybody.'

And I thought, Yes, it could. And it has. And I'm not the only one. Davy had given me one more reason, the best reason of all, to be glad he was living in our house. And then, with two sentences, he took it away again: 'Ah don't mean *I* wet it,' he said. 'It was the rain comin' in that leaky oul' skylight.'

It still leaks a bit, that skylight, and every time I lever it up on its rusty hinges I'm terrified that the whole pane is going to break off and go crashing down and brain somebody in the street. But at least *I* don't leak any more. I'm fit to sleep in a bed without a rubber sheet; man enough to lie in the wee front attic without fearing a visit from the bogey man.

I love that room. Of all the bedrooms in the house – of the six full-time ones, anyway – it's my favourite. Even if there's no space for anything but the bed and the wardrobe and the chest and the washhand basin. I like the way the ceiling slopes with the roof, and the way the sun draws skylight shapes on the bedclothes. There's no view but sky when you're standing in it, but if you kneel on the bed and press your nose against the glass you can see halfway to Portrush. God, I must be getting soft. Next thing you know I'll be writing a poem about it.

But I do hate having to give it up in the summer. If Davy Murray was still alive, and knocked on the door in July, I'd find it hard to move out even for him. He must have had it for two or three years, but I never think of it as his. It's funny that his name's not part of the furniture of the house; that there's a 'Miss Lambert's Room' but no 'Davy's Room'.

Three

Miss Lambert.

Weren't we polite in those days? Maisie, I'm sure, wishes it was still like that. My Ma's the only one now who ever calls her Mrs McCann. She can just about put up with familiarity from the rest of us, but she does get on her high horse if she thinks we've forgotten she's a paying guest. She expects her wee privileges. She makes it damn plain, for example, that she considers that corner of the settee nearest the fire to be hers and hers alone. We all know that now, so she has no need to be sprinkling fag ash to mark out her territory. And then, as my Ma would put it in her cod hoity-toity voice, she's so *refeened* in other ways. 'A mug? Oh, I couldn't drink out of a mug, dear. Have ye lost mae china cup?' And then there's the other favourite: 'Mrs Kerr, I think somebody's given me margarine by mistake. Must have been one of the boys –

you know I never eat anythin' but butter.' And more often that not it *is* one of us, and we do it out of what my Ma would call 'divilment'.

What would Maisie think if she knew what used to go on in that room of hers – Tom Canham, a married man, sneaking down to have it away with Brenda Lynch, a married woman? She'd have heart failure – like he did in the end.

Or would she? She'll probably outlast the lot of us. She's been here at least four years and from the look of her when she gets in that corner she's here to stay. We'll move on and somebody else'll take over the place; somebody who's never heard of Miss Lambert and who'll start calling the room above the hall 'Mrs McCann's Room'.

Miss Lambert. It makes her sound like an old maid; frumpy, horn-rimmed. But my Ma says she was young when she arrived. And as she didn't stay long she must have been young when she left.

There'd have been the usual five minutes of goodbyes at the porch:

'Now don't you forget me, Michael.'

'Ah won't.'

'Promise?'

'Promise. Cross mae heart and hope tae die.'

But I have forgotten her. Me with the great memory; me the star of the school quizzes. I can bring back the first line of my O-level French textbook: '*Les Français prennent, généralement, trois repas par jour: le petit déjeuner, le déjeuner et le dîner.*' But I can't bring back Miss Lambert.

She was a librarian in Coleraine, and I can picture her reading to me, so I like to think she introduced me to books. I remember loving her, or at least I loved the sweets she gave me. But I don't remember her face. It's gone for ever – along with Anne Mullan and Phyllis Canny. They're just two more names now, two more girls in the same grey skirt and blue cardigan going to the convent with Patricia.

If her face had been big and round, with a hat on top like an upturned soup bowl, like Nurse Gilmour's, I'd have remembered. If it had been like Tommy Nicholl's and put me in mind of the picture of the baddie in *Little Red Riding Hood*, I'd have remembered. (Poor Tommy: I'm not sure he'd be pleased to know that the first time I saw him I took him for a wolf. Not a nice thing to say about one of your neighbours – especially if you're a Cat and he's a Prod.) No. *I* know how I would have remembered: if her face had looked like her bloody dog's, the way an owner's face is supposed to, I'd never, ever, have forgotten it. Suki. A Pekinese. A bad wee bitch.

I didn't like her from that first minute I saw her skittering about on the tiles in the porch. 'Michael, isn't she a cute wee article?' my Ma said, bending to stroke her, and the cute wee article tried to leave its teeth in her arm. Miss Lambert told her off, apologized to my Ma, said that Suki was always like this at the start, that she would come round. But she didn't. And neither did we.

'Miss Lambert's a lovely wee person,' my Ma used to say, 'but I can't take to that animal. There's a terrible oul' smell in that room that Ah can't get out of the carpet. Ah'm sure that bloomin' thing's peed in the corner.'

My Da maintained it wasn't a dog at all. 'It's just a fur mat wi' teeth.' After a couple of days of trying to make friends, when all he got for his trouble was a growl and a snap, he gave up. 'That thing – huh! It would eat ye as soon as look at ye.'

Maybe that's why I mixed up the Suki in Miss Lambert's room with the Suki in the nursery rhyme.

> *Polly put the kettle on,*
> *Polly put the kettle on . . .*
> *Suki take it off again,*
> *We all run away.*

The nonsense that gets inside your head when you're a kid... Who the hell were Polly and Suki? And why were they messing about with a kettle? Christ knows. But I knew the Suki in our house was a bad one, and most of the time I stayed well out of her way.

My Ma was ironing that day in the kitchen. I would have been on my way to fight a fire, driving that battered Dinky engine through the streets of the town that lay between the kitchen door and the scullery door. I loved that engine. *Na-na, na-na, na-na.* I looked up now and again to watch my Ma, the tongue peeping out from the side of her mouth the way it does when she's concentrating. She's always teased the rest of us about that – 'It's all in the way ye hold yer mouth' – but she can't help doing it herself. She was just coming to the end, placing four or five of Miss Lambert's floral hankies, pressed into triangles, next to my Da's big striped squares.

'There, that'll do for now. Michael, darlin', would ye take these up and put them in Miss Lambert's room for me?'

But Suki was up there...

'It'll be all right, darlin'. Ah was in just a minute ago maesel'. She's asleep. She'll not touch ye.'

I took the hankies up, set them on the dressing table and was turning to leave when I felt something brush against my foot. I looked down and there was Suki, under the dressing table, head cocked to one side. She started to whine. It wasn't a scary sound; it was a sad one. I decided she was missing Miss Lambert. I lay down full length to stroke her.

'There, there,' I said, just as my Ma had done when the turkey tried to eat me. 'Don't worry. Miss Lambert'll be home soon.'

She carried on whining. She needed a cuddle. I reached in to pick her up, and as I did she lunged at me. Our eyes were level and as she came at me she seemed to be all hair and teeth. The teeth sank into my right arm. I shot back, banged my head on the dressing table, and came down those stairs as if the bogey man himself was chasing me.

My Ma rushed from the kitchen. 'Whatinunder-God. . . ?'

'Suki bit me. Suki bit me.'

'Where.'

'Here.'

Teethmarks. Blood. My Ma dabbing with a hankie. 'Come on, now, let's give it a quick wash an' then get ye a wee bun. There'll not be a word about it the day ye're gettin' married.'

Maybe she's right. Maybe there won't be. But the scare wasn't as easily dabbed away as the wound. After that, there wasn't a sweet in the world that would tempt me anywhere near Miss Lambert's room. When she eventually left, when she went off to marry that giant of a man named Mr Small, I missed her. But I was glad to see the back of Suki. My Da was right: she was the worst boarder we'd had yet.

And who was the best? I'm not sure there was one. Not at that stage, anyway. Uncle Peter and Aunt Winnie hadn't been over yet from England to stay. I was still too young to be finding friends among the visitors' children, to be drawing them into sword fights or football matches on the Harbour Hill. But not too young to be rolling my boiled egg down the Easter Egg Hill.

I wonder if any other families did that on Easter Sunday... It seems daft now – to spend all morning painting faces on boiled eggs only to roll them down a hill and crack them open. It took ages to get the eyes, nose and mouth right. And then mine rolled away from me and I lunged after it, missed and waited for the splat! Next thing I knew the egg was in my Da's hand, and then I was on his shoulders, and he was bouncing me to the top of the hill so I could send the egg on its way through the grass. Roll. Stop. Lift. Roll. I can see myself at the bottom peeling the shell, and pulling blades of grass from my teeth, and fretting about what my Ma had told me: if I didn't have at least one taste of the real egg, then there'd be no chocolate one for me when I got home.

I loved those hills. 'Up the mount'n',' I'd say, tugging at the hand of Mary McAleer or Nurse Gilmour, and away we'd go on an expedition. I couldn't figure out how Mary could be my Da's niece *and* a grown woman. All the other nieces I knew weren't much bigger than Bredge or myself. They had long hair, and, if they could be persuaded to sit still long enough, my Ma turned it into ringlets for them by twisting it round torn-off strips of the *Irish News*. Mary had short hair and a cap, and that upside-down watch on a pin that she'd hold next to my ear.

'Tick-tock. Tick-tock. Time I was back at the hospital. All right – just one quick race to the top an' back down.' But she never went too fast, and if I got tired she'd give me a piggyback.

Not like Nurse Gilmour. She was a route marcher. 'Come on,' she'd say, one hand clamping that upturned soup bowl on her head, 'we'll see nothin' at all before the rain if you don't pick them legs up. Race ye to the top.'

I'd follow her, stumbling, feet tripping over each other or over those grass-covered rocks. Then we'd be up at the top, the wind whipping at us, and we'd stop to catch our breath and gather seapinks for my Ma. Over on the right the hill sloped steeply down, to the road and steps, and more steps down to the Herring Pond, where the girls went swimming and came back with chattering teeth and goose pimples. Straight ahead was the lighthouse – not a pepperpot like the one in that colouring book of mine, but a squat, square whitewashed block, topped by a flashing light and a T-shaped mast.

'That's the fella keeps the ships safe,' Nurse Gilmour said. 'They'll not be runnin' on to the rocks when that's there.'

The rocks were dangerous. The waves were dangerous. I loved watching the waves, but I was scared of them, too; even more scared than I was of the bogey man, who lived in the big understairs cupboard. For I knew that the waves swept wee boys into the harbour and out to sea.

'Just like that,' my Ma said, driving the floor brush across the tiles.

But I wasn't scared when I was with Mary. Not even that first time when she took me by the hand right to the edge of the cliff and showed me the whole world.

Well, as much of the world as you can squeeze on to a postcard like the one on the window-sill. What else is here? My Ma's envelope for the collection on Sunday and a thank-you note from those nuns she sends money to in Devon (how did *they* get to hear she was a soft touch?). Peter must have found the card in somebody's room and brought it down − after he'd finished Vimming the washhand basin; after he'd hoked about among the dirty tissues and the dripping shampoo sachets (and other things we make sure our Ma doesn't see) to find the empty Coke or lemonade bottle that he could get five pence for in Herbisons' or Scilleys'. Sean and I are far too grand for pickings like those now, but we'd have been glad of them once.

It's not a great photograph. The lighting's flat. It was probably taken around the middle of the day. But I can picture Mary and myself standing where the photographer was standing (except he was probably kneeling, with his camera on a tripod, for there's none of the softness that results from the hand shakes that I get). I can see Mary pointing, and hear her voice: 'Look. That's the harbour down there, where the fish comes in for yer Friday dinner. An' that green hut up there is where some of the boys and girls have their lessons because there's not enough room in the proper school. And that's the Prom, with Morelli's ice-cream shop in the middle of it, an' the town hall at the far end an' the chapel. Ye see right at the end of it – that buildin' that looks like a castle? That's the convent where Judette goes. An' over there's the Strand, an' farther along, the hills o' Donegal. Isn't that lovely?'

And she extends an arm towards it again, all of it, as if it's mine, a present she's just bought for me.

Aye, I was easily pleased in those days. I made magic mountains out of common hillocks. After a while, when I got a sense of proportion, the Mountain became the Green Hill. And then I went to school, and saw it on the map, and discovered that it was really the Harbour Hill.

My Ma's gone through a similar transformation. First she was Mammy, then Mummy and now she's nearly always Mum. To her face anyway – though when I'm talking about her to people of my own age she's still 'mae Ma'; there's something uncomfortable on the tongue, something English, about 'my Mum'.

I've been putting away childish things, but maybe I've been putting away Catholic ones, too. And I'm sure it all started when I was in short trousers on the Harbour Hill. If the wee boys you're playing with all scream for 'Mummy' when they fall over and graze their knees, then unless you're very thick-skinned you're not going to carry on screaming for Mammy. So our Catholic Mammy, without changing her ways at all, became Protestant Mummy.

But it was probably English TV that turned her into Mum. Mum this, Mum that, Mum the other. The only ones on TV who called for 'Mummy' were spoilt wee brats on the backs of ponies, and we had nothing in common with them at all.

Ponies? We'd have settled for bikes. What were those

28

things my Da made Sean and me when we started running round the back yard? I'm not sure there's even a name for them. There was a long piece of thick wire, almost piping, shaped into a handle at one end and an axle on the other. My Da hung a wheel on the axle and fixed it with a nut so it would turn. We whizzed up and down, pushing the wheels in front of us, winning and losing races. 'Cowboys now,' Sean would say, and we'd be John Wayne and The Virginian in the endless prairies between the door of the toilet and the window-sill of the breakfast room. 'North-West 200,' I'd say, and – whee! – the pair of us would be riders in the motorcycle races, screaming round Henry's Corner on our 500cc Nortons, our knees a hair's breadth from tarmac. Cecil would lean over the wall, chin on his arms, and eye us as dolefully as a basset hound.

'Are ye havin' fun, boys?'

'Aye, Mr Hall, great fun. How ye doin', Mr Hall? How's Winnie?'

That was in the days when Winnie was always making too many chips – was it accidentally on purpose? – and then shouting over the wall for one of us to come and collect them. She'd be jumping up and down on the top step because she was too short to see over the top of the wall. 'Are there any o' you Kerrs alive in there? Come an' get these chips before they're all cold.' They couldn't be more different, the pair of them: she's small and wiry, full of fun and jokes; he's a big imposing man, but shy as a wean and careful with his words. I suppose the job taught him that.

'Now you boys behave yourselves, for ye're living next door to a policeman now,' my Ma used to say when Sean and I were hardly old enough for primary school, let alone borstal. Then there was the other favourite: 'It's Sunday, remember, and ye're not tae be kickin' football. Ah don't want ye annoyin' the neighbours.' Annoying the *Protestant* neighbours, she meant. She knew that Sunday in those days really was a day of rest for them. Not many things have changed in Portstewart since we were weans, but that's one of them. You don't have to sit in all Sunday afternoon watching James Stewart films once the dinner's over. You can kick a ball about without worrying that somebody's going to get upset about it.

My Ma still likes to kid herself that the neighbours were foxed for a while after we moved in, that they weren't sure what we were because of the name. *New neighbours – wonder what they are . . . Catholic? Naw, not with a name like that. Kerr. Scottish. Must be stout Protestant stock like ourselves.*

I wonder. That doesn't tie in with the story she used to tell of Ian and Mervyn Nicholl greeting us by chucking stones in the porch. Did they do that because they knew something we thought they hadn't yet tumbled to? I mean, did they chuck those stones as bad wee boys or did they chuck them as bad wee Protestant boys?

I can remember exactly how I put it in that short story, because it was the first thing I wrote that wasn't done for a teacher; the first thing I did just because I had something in my head that I wanted to get down on paper:

It was an hour or two after Miss Lambert's arrival and I was engaged in my favourite occupation of watching the world from a window. I was up in the sitting room. I saw two boys come running up to our front wall. They stopped at the wall, looking closely at the front window as if to make sure there was no one in the dining room. Then they fired a hail of stones into the porch. I ran downstairs to report the news, but my father and mother were already in the hall.

'What in the name o' God was that?' said my mother.

'It was them boys from up the road,' I told her. 'They were throwin' stones.'

My father opened the front door and began picking the stones off the tiles. 'Look at the size o' that,' he said, holding one of them up. 'It's a damn good job it didn't hit the glass.'

'Did ye see them, love?' my mother asked.

'Aye,' I said. 'It was them boys from up the road.'

'Are ye sure?'

'Aye, Ah saw them. Why did they do that, Mammy?'

'Bad wee brats,' said my father. 'I know rightly why they did it. For two pins Ah'd – '

'Mick, they're only weans,' said my mother.

'Aye, maybe they are,' said my father. 'And maybe it's coincidence that they picked the only Catholic porch in the street.'

'You be careful where ye leave that lyin' around,' my Ma said.

'It's only a story,' I told her.

'Aye, but . . .'

I asked whether that was how she remembered it.

'Aye. Is that the way you remember it?'

I said it was. But that was a lie. I didn't remember it at all. I'd taken her bald report that Ian and Mervyn had thrown stones into our porch and turned it into a piece of fiction. At the time I was delighted that it captured her memory. I was even more delighted that she thought something written down on paper could be dangerous. Now I know I was being a stupid prick. All I was doing was reminding her about an incident she should have forgiven and forgotten, making her think badly of the Nicholls. There was I, the smart-arse who lectured the rest of the family about Irish myths, and I was creating one of my own.

I didn't see any stone-throwing. Ian and Mervyn never threw stones at me. Their wee brother threw clods of earth at me regularly and I threw them back. That's what wee boys do when they're fighting the Second World War all over again. My clods were British grenades, Adrian's were German.

And what about Ian and Mervyn's stones? Who knows? Maybe the Nicholls *didn't* like Catholics when we moved in. But they've got used to us over the years. 'The best o' neighbours,' as my Ma says. 'Always ready to help out if ye're in a jam.' Which is what Mervyn's going to be doing for me on Tuesday.

I'm sure he and his Ma and Da knew rightly as soon as we arrived that we were Catholic. They only had to hear us calling each other in for our tea. Judette, Roisin, Bredge – bit of a giveaway those names, aren't they? And to be a hundred per cent certain which foot we kicked with, all they had to do was take one look in the kitchen.

Four

More tea, vicar?

Oh, no. I'm catching it, too. Sean's got into the habit of saying that when he's pouring us a mug and now I'm doing it. Doing it when I talk to myself – even worse. Still, I'd like to see it: a vicar sitting where I'm sitting. I don't think he'd be terribly comfy.

Would he come in at all? Would he get past that plastic Our Lady by the light-switch cord at the door, her feet pointing to the sponge soaked in Lourdes water? (My Ma's standards are slipping: the sponge is nearly dry.) He might miss it, I suppose. But if he was sitting where I'm sitting he could hardly avoid looking at the Sacred Heart, propped on that shelf behind the clock.

I'd never really looked at it myself – not properly looked at it – until Mick Rafferty asked us to do that essay on 'Things We Take For Granted'. Even if you only glance at it, of course, you remember that Jesus is not only long-nosed and long-faced but also long-haired – as we always reminded our Ma when she was sending us to Johnny Stevenson to be scalped. But you have to study it a while to remember details like the position of the hands: the left palm up in the air facing outwards, the right stretched forward as if He's welcoming you in. But I don't think the vicar would find it very welcoming, not with that brownish-purple heart ringed by thorns and dripping blood. I know they don't have that sort of thing in Protestant churches, even if I don't know what they do have. The lamp in front of the picture reminds me of an upturned test tube, or at least it would if it wasn't red with a silver cross inside. The Sacred Heart and the lamp, positioned next to the clock – the 'temporal beside the spiritual', as I put it in the essay. Rafferty underlined that bit and wrote 'Excellent' in the margin. Bollocks. It's pretentious shit and he knew it.

The Sacred Heart's never moved, but the Kennedys have. They used to hang on the wall on this side, Jack and Bobby in profile. I suppose they went up some time after Bobby's shooting, when we were still being told that they were two good Irish Catholics who might have changed the world for the better, two heroes for the Kerr boys to look up to as we supped our porridge. But when did they come down? And why? Did my Ma finally discover it wasn't only affairs of state they conducted in their offices? Or did she just unhook them one time when my Da was painting and forget to put them back?

No danger of that happening to the Pope. But he still doesn't look too pleased. It's almost as if the clash is annoying him — those rosary beads of my Ma's hanging from the hook and dangling over the ones round his neck. John Paul II. Roman numerals for a Roman Catholic, as I thought it used to go. He's shown more staying power than his predecessor. 'What's the difference between the Pope and a fruit gum?' was the great one at school at that time. Answer: A fruit gum lasts longer. When we moved in, of course, John XXIII had come with us from Heathmount in Uncle Jimmy's van and he went into the window recess, until he died and Paul VI took over. Paul the Sick I thought everybody was saying, and I wasn't a bit surprised, because the job had killed the man who had it before him. I prayed that he'd get better. *Every night before I sleep I pray to God my soul to keep. If I die before I wake I pray to God my soul to take. God bless Mammy and Daddy and all our family and please fix Granny's bad leg and make the Pope better.*

I was a terrible worrier about people's health in those days. I worried even about Martin Douglas, though the first time I saw him, through the sitting-room window, I thought he was hilarious. With those semicircles of black hair over his ears he looked like Coco the Clown, though he didn't dress as brightly: white shirt, black tie, grey cardigan and blue nylon jacket. He came out through the front door, sniffed the air and walked to the gate. He stopped for a minute, folded his broad hairy arms and surveyed the street from top to bottom as if he owned it. Then he turned sharp left and marched off, right arm up in the air, palm flat, as if he was carrying an invisible tray. He wasn't gone more than five minutes. When he came back into view, the arm was still up in the air, the hand now closed round a tin of peas.

'Who was that funny man, Mammy?'

'Poor Martin. Ye mustn't laugh at 'im. It's a pity o' the oul' crettur.'

'What's wrong wi' 'im?'

'The poor thing's soft in the head. Ah don't know what woulda happened tae him if his sister hadn't taken him in.'

I didn't laugh at Martin after that – well, not every time I saw him – and I worried about his soft head and the chances of something falling on it when he was out and about with his invisible tray. But I didn't say any prayers for him; I knew he was a Protestant and they would do no good.

What was that phrase in the old history textbook? 'Religion pervaded all activities . . .' That's the way it used to be here. It still is for my Ma. When my Da gets a shock or a scare and comes out with 'Jesus, Mary and Joseph!' it just sounds like he's swearing. But when my Ma does it, it's as if she's really asking for help.

She's still a powerful prayer, but she seems to have given up trying to make the rest of us say the Rosary. It kind of takes you by surprise when she does it now. Not like the old days in the winter. As soon as whoever was staying had gone out for the evening, she'd put down the jumper she was knitting or the trousers she was hemming. 'Right, you bunch o' heathens,' she'd say, 'turn off that oul' television. It's time we were at the Rosary.'

'Och, Mammy, it was just gettin' to the good bit . . .' But we knew there was no postponing all those Our Fathers and Hail Marys, let alone escaping them. If my Da hadn't already gone to the Anchor he'd be down on his knees too, elbows resting on the cushion of his armchair, feet splayed to show us those woolly pads at the bottom of his thermal socks.

It's never been him who starts the prayers, always my Ma. She's the holy one, she'd give up everything for God, but he has trouble giving up the drink for Lent. There was that time he said he wouldn't touch whiskey, and he didn't, not once. He drank gin instead. And she maintained for ages afterwards that he snored less on it.

The Rosary isn't the only thing they've got more relaxed about. The pair of them still rise as early as ever on a Sunday, but they don't seem to mind if the rest of us only make it to the chapel by eleven. Time was when my Ma would have had everybody out for the half eight, all of us fasting so we could go to communion. A state of grace: I wondered then how that was different from the grace we said before meals; the grace everybody said even quicker than usual on Sunday because we were all ravenous when we got back home for breakfast. *BlessusOLordandthesethygifts . . .*

In winter we were frozen as well as ravenous. We still are – it's going to be great at college to have the central heating. We should light the range before Mass and then the house wouldn't be so icy. When you get out of bed and look in the mirror your breath mists it over – which is maybe just as well considering the shape I'm in sometimes after a night at Kelly's. But at least these days there's none of that motherly pummelling with a cold facecloth. 'Did ye not wash yersel' before ye went tae bed? Here, let me look in that ear. An' the other one. It's a good scrub ye need, not this lick-an'-a-promise. But ye'll have tae do. Now, have ye got a hankie? Well, what did ye do with it? Ah gave ye one last night. Here, take one o' yer Daddy's . . .'

In those days we'd walk on the sea side of the Prom and see nobody from one end of it to the other, no living thing but the gulls, banking and diving and bombing the helmet of the soldier on the war memorial. It was a long walk when your legs were as short as mine. If it had been any other day, and any other time, I could have done my 'poor tired wee boy' act and got one of the girls to give me a piggyback. But not on Sundays before breakfast. They were all fasting, and they were too cold and hungry to be bothered. 'Come *on*, Michael!'

I miss the Latin Mass now it's gone, but I didn't like it much then, didn't know what the hell was going on. My Ma told me to watch her so I would know when I should be standing or kneeling or sitting. When I started to fiddle she'd lean down, that black-lace mantilla brushing against the side of my face, pinch me just above the knee and whisper 'Up ye get, now' or 'Down on yer knees.' The kneeler was hard and made dents on my bare legs. When I leant forward, I'd find my mouth on a level with the back rail of the seat in front, and I'd nibble on it. The varnish was like a toffee apple without the sugar.

My Ma gave me a right poke in the cheek when she caught me at that. And she got annoyed with me when she saw me looking round for my Da. But I couldn't help it. She'd march us up the aisle to the same place every Sunday, as if that pew halfway down the chapel on the left-hand side had her name on it, and as soon as we were settled in the seat I'd have to have a look round for him. She'd told me why he always stayed at the back – 'because he doesn't like being hemmed in an' he has tae help the

St Vincent de Paul wi' the collection' – and I understood, but I wasn't sure that other people would understand. I didn't want them thinking we'd had a row in the house and nobody was speaking to him.

'Daddy's comin',' I whispered when he began striding up the aisle with the big brown plate like a soup bowl. (Why did they do away with them, I wonder? Did they clink too much? Or is it that you can get more into a basket?) My Ma shushed me. As he got close to our pew, she passed me the envelope from her handbag so that I could drop it on the plate. But she never looked sideways, never gave any sign that she noticed the wink he gave us as he passed. She just knelt there with the hands steepled and the rosary beads wound round them, with eyes for nothing but the altar.

When Mass was over... well, in Latin it was just over, the last prayer was as sombre as the first. But things were different after we switched to English. '*The Mass is ended. Thanks be to God,*' was sometimes the most heartfelt prayer of the lot. It was hardly a sin, was it, when you were as hungry as we were?

We'd be dragging my Ma through the porch and she'd be dallying to chew the fat with Mrs Diamond or somebody else she only ever bumped into on a Sunday, or wasting her money on the cheesy mix of recipes and homilies in *Ireland's Own*. I don't know why she bothered. Even she got little good out of it, and it found its way quicker than most of its kind under the cushion of this armchair. What's here now? Half of a back page from the *Chronicle* with Danny in the front row of the Dominican football team. At least the caption says it's

Danny; his face is so dark with ink he might be one of the Black and White Minstrels. A copy of the *Messenger*, and one of the *Far East*: 'Remember The Missions. Please Give Generously.'

We used to do that, all right. I hadn't been at school long when Mrs Boyle started the collections for the black babies and the white babies. 'Ye'd think we didn't have enough white babies of our own tae look after,' my Ma said, but I knew she was only joking, and the following day I had my penny to hand in. The black babies, I knew, were the ones the missionaries went to with milk powder in one hand and a missal like my Ma's in the other. But Mrs Boyle was vaguer about the white babies. Deliberately, I'm sure. We were a bit young to be learning about Catholic girls who *got themselves in trouble* and needed to be sent away to have their babies on the QT in some gothic horror run by nuns. Just think, if Anne and David hadn't got married, and she'd still insisted on having Karen, she'd probably have been sent away. And some other wee boys in primary one would have been collecting pennies for the nuns so they could feed my sister's white baby.

When I picture us all sitting down to dinner on Sunday, it is *all* of us: five girls, four boys – one in a high-chair – father at the head of the table, mother on his right-hand side. But it can't have been like that for long. When was it Judette was born? 1949. And Peter not until '66. Seventeen years between them. He hadn't even started school when she left home that summer to work in the hotel on the Isle of Man. And the people who'd hired her were so impressed they had my Ma and Da over for a week's free holiday and then offered to buy Judette her own boarding house there. She's a natural, they said, she'll coin it. My Ma and Da said no, she was too young, it was too much responsibility. But they were still full of it, proud as hell of their great wee worker.

We were all great wee workers. We had to be. There was no dodging it. It sounds like it was easier to get out of Vietnam than it was to get out of helping here. From morning to night in summer the girls were never off the batter. What were they *on*, I wonder? How did they keep going? It wasn't just B & B in those days; it was breakfast, dinner, tea and supper. God knows how they found the puff in the evenings to sing 'Ebony Eyes'.

Sean and I did our bit, too. We weren't strong enough to lift the coal bucket, and we couldn't be trusted with china or glass, but we could bundle sticks in the yard as fast as our Da felled them with the hatchet. We could howl for our Ma at the first spot of rain so she could whip the sheets off the line and get them inside. And we could run a greedy finger round the mixing bowl when she'd finished the baking. There was nothing better than a bun straight from the oven, a pancake straight from the griddle, but you had to be patient, and we were anything but. *Are they done? Are they done?* I must have spent a good few hours of my life standing by the range with my tongue hanging out.

The engine of the house – that's what the range is, even if it doesn't look much like one. A great creamy slab with a black-leaded top. But it boils the water, bakes the bread, roasts the meat. Its hot breath warms the plate rack – where, of course, we've never kept anything but folded clothes – and dries all those shirts and smalls hanging on the airer. It makes the whole kitchen cosy – except when it's having a blow-down and belching out black smoke round the white washing. 'This bloomin' oul' range...' my Ma mutters, but she'll soon have it fixed. She knows its needs and moods and quirks. That thermometer on the front of the oven door has never worked, and she's never missed it. If she wants to know how hot the oven is, she feels the door. Just to be sure she might open it, feel the oven's breath round her legs, maybe touch a hand to one of the shelves. I see her shaking her head. No, she says, it needs a bit longer, another shovel of coal, a wee poke. Hand me that poker.

Those hands of hers... She's forever wiping and washing and polishing, stirring and scrubbing and steeping, dipping them in starch and bleach. They look twenty years older than she does. But she never complains. We're the ones who do that.

Five

The junk on this window-sill! Where does it all come from? Recipes my Ma's torn from magazines, odd buttons, dried-out pens, a pattern for a jumper ('Knit a smart sweater for a young playboy') and an airmail letter from Bredge. I didn't know we'd had a letter from Bredge. Well, if you can call it a letter. It's her usual six-liner, the literary equivalent of my Ma's lick-an'-a-promise with the facecloth. Hardly started before it's ended. 'There's not much news and I've got to get back to work so I'll have to sign off here. I'm enclosing a photo from the film I shot at home. Love to everybody, Bredge.'

Here she is, standing at the side of the range, arm round my Da. If you didn't know her, if you didn't know that as a kid she used to mop the floor she's standing on (when she couldn't batter me into doing it), you'd think she was one of the visitors. A model, maybe, in one of those shots where the beautiful people are posed in peasant houses next to the horny-handed. The flash glares off the tiles and off the green gloss my Da slapped on the walls because he'd been given a couple of tins of it and my Ma said it would do just as well as emulsion and sure nobody would ever notice. My Da's cardigan's rumpled and his hair's sticking up at the back; he looks as if he's only just been roused from the armchair. But Bredge, in that beautifully tailored emerald suit, beaming her big white teeth, looks like a film star – even though there are two big woolly socks hanging from the airer just beside her head.

When she was home she had so many clothes with her we thought Qantas must have put on a second plane to carry them. Most of them were new, bought specially for the trip. But Anne only had to say that this was a lovely blouse or that was a gorgeous skirt and Bredge would be offering to hand it over there and then. 'Go on – keep it. I hardly ever wear it anyway.' The girls are always like this now when they get together: swapping clothes as easily as they swap stories. It's hard to believe they used to claw each other over a jacket or a jumper. But that's the way it was in those summers in the early Sixties; before the house was full of visitors it was full of arguments. They'd got used to the luxury of space during the winter and they weren't keen on piling themselves and all their stuff into one room again.

'Do we have to, Mammy?' Roisin or Judette would ask.

'Yes, love. There's nothin' else for it.'

'Well, I'm not sleepin' anywhere near Bredge. She kicks the life out o' ye. And she snores like a bog eel.'

'Ah do not.'

'Ye do so.'

'That's enough from the pair o' ye. Now, take the clothes out o' this wardrobe and move them in next door, and put the rest o' that stuff intae cardboard boxes.'

And so the packing began, and the grumbles about 'the bloomin' visitors' and the claims and counter-claims. Anne looked into a box Trish had almost filled and recognized a flash of fabric.

'Patricia, that's my blouse.'

'Where?'

'That one.'

'But you gave me it that day we were goin' to Jennifer's party.'

'God forgive ye! Ah said ye could have the loan of it.'

'An' then ye said Ah could hang on to it cause ye never wore it anyway.'

'Ah did *not*! That's the only one that goes wi' mae brown skirt.'

'All right, then. Have yer oul' blouse!' And Trish hauled it out in such a temper that she tossed half her own things with it on to the floor.

And so it went on for what seemed ages, with a row every ten minutes over this blouse or that dress. 'Are you girls nearly done up there?' my Ma yelled from the landing below. 'Ah coulda had them boxes packed maesel' ten times over by now.'

Not that she and my Da would have been doing a whole lot better. Humping the furniture around tends to remind them of when and how they bought it – usually at some auction at Gordon's where she thinks she got a bargain and he thinks she got conned.

'They musta seen you comin' when they sold ye this oul' chest. It's fit for nothin' but the dump.'

'Away outta that.There's a good few years left in it yet.'

And it's surprising how long the stuff lasts, seeing how often it gets dragged around the rooms and up and down the stairs.Though there's been a bit less of that in the past few years.There's not much point in moving all of us out if there's hardly any visitors to move in. 'Sure people are terrified to come,' my Ma says. 'And who can blame them, when they see the streets full o' them boys throwin' petrol bombs? Civil rights? There's none o' them looks very civil tae me.' And I want to argue with her and say that you can't blame the protesters if their protest is hijacked by guys with guns, but I don't because deep down I think she's right – that things might have been bad before but they're a hell of a lot worse now. Still, easy for me to say that. I've never had the experience the girls have had. I've never gone along for a job and been turned down just because I happened to be a Catholic.

Imagine if we did that here. 'Hello, Mr Kojak.Yes, I'm sure we can find you a bed for the night, but first I've got to ask you one wee question. Are you a Cat or a Prod?' There'd have been a lot less furniture-moving and a lot more sleeping in our own beds if we'd done that.

But it would be a lie to say it's never been fun.The first year I was old enough to help it was a real adventure doing a flit inside our own house. I couldn't wait to get all our stuff out of the bedroom and down to the breakfast room. I raced up and down, tripping over pillows, spilling Dinky cars through the gaps between the banisters, generally getting in the way.

But eventually it was all done. The room upstairs was

cleared. Only the beds were left. Stripped of clothes and mattresses, they were all hard wood and ringing metal. The spring on the one Sean and I shared had a big rusty stain in the middle.

'What's that?'

My Ma gave me a half-smile. 'You should know, ye boy ye.'

'Did somebody burn it?'

'Naw, nobody burned it. That's what happens when wee boys need tae go to the toilet and don't get up in time tae do it.'

While my Ma held one end of the bed, my Da got down on one knee and took a spanner to the nuts and bolts holding the rails. When he had lifted both rails off, she moved the end away and leaned it against the wall. They did the same at the other end and on the other bed. Then they carried the rails and ends downstairs.

Finally, they moved the springs, easing each one out the door, down the stairs and round the banisters. I looked on from the landing, watching them wobble about because there was no weight in the middle, only in the wood.

''Asy, 'asy, darlin'', my Da said as he led the way down the stairs. 'Ye'll have me over this banister on mae mouth an' nose!' When he stepped down into the hall, he had to squeeze into the corner among the girls' coats hanging on their hooks. He pulled one over each shoulder and grinned out from between them. 'How dae Ah look?'

'Suits ye down to the groun',' she told him. 'Now, when ye're finished actin' the cod can we get this thing intae the breakfast room before it breaks my back?'

When both springs were down they reassembled the beds and made them. I was glad to see that shameful stain covered by a mattress. My Da tucked in the last corner, then drew himself up to his full height, bowed in front of me and held his open right hand towards the bed. 'Would sir like to try it?'

He was acting the cod again, and he wanted me to join in. I went to climb up on the bed. He coughed like a butler. 'Ah think sir might be more comfortable without his shoes.' I pulled the shoes off without undoing the laces, knowing that this time I wouldn't be told off, and scrambled up. I lay back with my hands clasped behind my head.

'Everythin' to sir's satisfaction?'

'Aye,' I said. 'Just the job. Ah'll take it.' I held out an imaginary note. 'Here ye are, fifty poun's.'

He took it, pocketed it. I was telling myself that moving rooms was a great game and it was a pity we couldn't do it more often when my Ma came over to the bed.

'Right, Michael, Ah've got somethin' tae tell ye. Until the summer's over you're tae stay out o' the sittin' room an' the dinin' room an' you're not tae be usin' that toilet upstairs. When ye want tae go, ye use the outside toilet. D'ye hear me?'

I'd heard all right and I didn't like the sound of it. No proper paper, just cut-offs from the *Irish News* hung on a nail. A door that didn't close tight, so somebody else might think the toilet was empty and try to join you just as you'd dropped your trousers. And sometimes when I was sitting on the seat I'd see a big spider abseiling down from its web. I hated it out there.

When the visitors started arriving, even the ones who were booked, they always seemed to catch us on the hop.

My Ma would have her hands in a scone- or cake-mix when one of the girls came in to announce that Mr and Mrs Irvine were here from Belfast or some Scottish family was asking about vacancies. She'd shake off the flour, fly to the sink in the scullery and run the tap on her hands. Passing again through the kitchen, she'd glance in the mirror, take a hairgrip out, clamp it in her teeth, tuck in an unruly lock and then jab the grip back.

'Look at the sight o' me.'

'Ye're all right, Mammy.'

And off she would dash to the door.

The dining room was always the place for the introductory chat, the word on mealtimes and charges. And Sean and I weren't supposed to go anywhere near it. But when we sidled in and hid behind my Ma's chair the girls couldn't very well drag us out kicking and screaming in front of the visitors. My Ma was a different woman in the dining room. It was as if she belonged in the kitchen, and she wasn't at home among all the shining cutlery and starched cloth. She took care with her words, pronouncing all their endings. 'Did you have trouble finding us?' she would say, not 'findin' us'. She wore her Sunday-go-to-meeting face, the stiff and serious one.

When she had helped the people upstairs with their cases and shown them round, she always said the same thing: 'If you need anything at all, just come to the kitchen and ask.' Sometimes they did. Sometimes there was a knock on the kitchen door and when one of the girls opened it I'd catch sight of a woman in a dressing gown asking whether there was enough hot water for her to have a bath. Then there was that time I was sent up with a towel to my Ma and Da's bedroom and forgot it wasn't their room any longer and went in without knocking. And there was that man lying on the covers in his long johns, the snores making his belly rise like Humpty Dumpty's.

Otherwise I hardly saw the visitors in those days. They weren't people so much as causes and effects. They were the reason I was barred from upstairs. It was for *them* that my Ma was buying so many tins of biscuits. It was them that had made Judette cry.

'Mammy, Mr Cox says his egg's too runny and could he have it a bit harder.'

'Of course, he can, darlin'. Tell 'im it'll just be a few minutes.'

'Mammy, Mrs Cox says the wheaten's hard.'

'But Ah only baked it this mornin'.'

'Ah know. Everybody else seems to be enjoyin' it.'

'All right. Ah'll cut a few slices from the other one and ye can take that in.'

And then: 'Judette, whatinunderGod's the matter? Why are ye cryin'?'

'That bloody oul' bugger. He told me off for reachin' over 'im tae put his soup down. An' Ah only did it because his brother wouldn't move in tae let me past.'

'Who told ye off?'

'Mr blinkin' Cox. Everybody else is so nice and the three of them are never done moanin'. "I'm afraid this isn't *quite* what we expect..." Every time he opens that big English mouth o' his he's grumblin' about somethin'.'

I hated the English for ages after that. I knew nothing about eight hundred years of Irish history and I hated them anyway. All because three of them had been snappy

with Judette in the dining room. If visitors were com-
plaining or giving us trouble then I just assumed they
must be English visitors, and I felt about them the way
Judette did: 'Ah can't wait till the buggers have gone. An'
Ah can't wait for September tae get back to school.'

Six

You're supposed to remember your first day at school, but it's the walk *to* school I remember, because my Ma was still angry about the frying steak.

John Lyons had been in the street making his rounds the day before. I'd been in the dining room looking out the window and had seen him get off his bike. I went in to tell my Ma in case she wanted to catch him and order something.

'There's nothin' I want from John,' she said. 'But you tell him to wait a wee minute, for I need tae have a word wi' 'im.'

So I did, and John followed me into the porch and stood there in his butcher's apron, running a hand through his silver hair, fiddling with the bicycle clips on his trousers, while he waited for my Ma to come to the door. Then he unclipped his satchel and reached for his notebook, flicking its pages over with one hand, fishing a pencil from his pocket with the other. 'How ye doin', Mrs Kerr? What can Ah get ye?' he said.

'Nothin' at all, John,' my Ma said. 'Certainly not the day, anyway. Ah'm very disappointed in ye.'

John looked as if he'd been slapped in the face. He lifted the flap on his satchel and dropped the notebook back inside. 'Why's that, Mrs Kerr?' he said. 'What have Ah done?'

My Ma told him she'd been far from pleased for a while with the meat he was giving her and hadn't said anything. 'But that fryin' steak yesterday was the worst yet. Ah coulda kicked it from here tae Derry without makin' a dent in it.'

John apologized, said that maybe he'd been leaving too much to John Junior and he would have a word with him when he got back to the shop. My Ma nodded and said she hoped he would, for she didn't want to have to start getting her meat from somebody else. She was civil enough to his face. But as soon as he'd ridden off and she'd closed the door she muttered: 'Huh. He wouldn't try offloadin' that oul' rubbish at any other house in the street.' Even then, I think, I knew what she meant. I didn't need telling that every other house in the street was Protestant.

We passed John's shop on the way to school. He was cleaving through a bone and he looked up, waved with his free hand, set down the cleaver and came to the open door. He moved quickly for a big man, his shoes like two shiny black boats on a sea of sawdust. 'Hello, Mrs Kerr. Hello, son,' he said. 'Do ye need anythin' the day, Mrs Kerr?'

My Ma said hello, told him she needed nothing right now, thank you, and hurried on. John stood there a moment, wiping his hands on his apron, and then went back inside.

I'd never seen my Ma that cold with anyone. I felt sorry for John. I asked whether she was going to stop buying meat from him.

She smiled. 'Maybe Ah'll drop in on the way home,' she said. 'But it'll do him no harm tae stew for a bit in the meantime.'

The walk was an education in itself. Across the road from John Lyons' shop, behind where Joe Campbell lived, was the Gospel Hall. My Ma said it was a church, which seemed unlikely to me because it was as plain as a garage, but she told me Protestant people weren't keen on ornaments. Passing down the side of it, we turned into Garden Avenue and saw, across the road, the playing field of Preston's, where I knew Mervyn Nicholl was going to school.

'That's Preston's field, isn't it?'

'Aye, son. But it's not really Preston's school. It's Portstewart Primary School. It's just that everybody calls it Preston's after the headmaster.'

On our own side of the road was the Ormo Bakery, whose fadge we had with our Sunday fry if my Ma had had no time to make her own. Past that we crossed the road and entered Convention Avenue.

'Ye've heard us talkin' about the Convention Tent,' my Ma said. 'Well, now ye can see for yersel' where they put it.'

She lifted me so I could look over the wall on our right, over the backs of the houses along the Prom and down to the bay. But there was no tent to be seen. 'All packed away now,' she said. 'It's only up for a couple of weeks in August. And ye know what happens then . . .'

'It rains all the time.'

'Aye,' she laughed. 'That's what they say, anyway. But Ah think we do rightly for rain at the best o' times in Portstewart.'

I'd seen the women in black bonnets and capes who arrived during the Convention and sang hymns on the steps above the beach, their voices snatched away by the wind and the waves. I knew they weren't Catholic, but I didn't think of them as Protestant, and I was too young then to know they were the Sally Army. I just thought they were a bit odd. I wondered if it rained because God didn't like their singing.

When we got to school, my Ma introduced me to Mrs Boyle. It was her hair I noticed first. It was like the candyfloss my Da had bought me the day we rode the bumper cars at Barrys, except that candyfloss was pink and her hair was nearly white. She and my Ma chatted a while. Then my Ma whispered something, Mrs Boyle nodded, and my Ma crooked her finger at me. I followed her down the corridor from the classroom, out through a set of glazed doors, and turned right. My Ma stopped and pointed at a sign over an entrance: BOYS.

'What d'ye think's in there?' she asked.

'The toilets?'

'Aye. An' now ye know where they are, ye've no excuse for doin' what Patricia did.'

Oh aye, we all know what Trish did – we've been told often enough. My Ma walks her to school on her first day, settles her in and goes home to get on with the day's work. A few hours later she's out sweeping the tiles in the porch when she sees Trish coming running towards her. Trish has been dying to go to the toilet and assumes she has no option but to go all the way home.

My Da's out of bed, thumping down to the toilet himself. That hit-and-run driver didn't leave him lame – there's no visible sign of injury – but when he's on the stairs I sometimes think I can hear a clunkiness in his step. The night it happened my Ma still had the shakes when she arrived home from the hospital. 'There 'e was, just goin' round tae get in the driver's seat, when this boy came flyin' round the corner. Absolutely flyin'. Yer Daddy went down and for a minute Ah couldn't even look at 'im. Ah was *sure* 'e was dead.' I felt guilty then and I feel guilty now, for as she was telling me all this I was thinking of the way my Da drives when he's tanked up, and how easily it could have been *him* clipping somebody as he came round a corner.

He's coughing – that *hack*, *hack*, *hack* that goes ahead of him everywhere like a town crier. I think it's that more than anything that's put me off smoking. My Ma thought getting him on to the filter-tips would have made a difference, but it hasn't. Not at all. He had the sixty-a-day Gallaher's Blues habit for far too long.

It was Greens Joe Fairley smoked. When he first sent me for them I felt sorry for him. There he was, a clever man, a great teacher, and he could only afford a packet of ten when my Da was always able to buy twenty. I was about eight then, but there were no flies on me. I stopped halfway down the road, climbed on the wall and had a nose in the backyards of the people who lived along the

Prom, thinking how great it would be if we had a cliff coming right down to *our* back door. I took the steps down to the Prom one at a time, bending down and weaving in and out under the handrail. The door of Morelli's was open, so I stuck my nose in and had a good sniff of the coffee. Then I went into McIntyre's, bought the cigarettes and dandered back. After that, knowing how long it took, I could sprint there, sprint back, and leave myself a few minutes in between to flick through *Charles Buchan's Football Monthly* and the *Hotspur* and the *Hornet*.

Imagine the fuss there'd be if a teacher sent a kid for cigarettes now... Maybe even in those days he'd have got a ticking-off if anybody had known. But nobody did know. Nobody but me and Joe Fairley. Joe with that goatee beard that made him the spitting image of Lenin in the school encyclopedia – except that Lenin was a bad Communist and Joe was a good Catholic. And I thought the sun shone out of his arse.

I liked Mrs Boyle at the start, too. 'A nice lady,' I told my Da once, when he should still have been encouraging me to think well of teachers. 'Lady Muck, more like,' he said. I think she must have been a bit grand with him when he was working at the school, when he was clerk of works on the extension and had his Portakabin in the playground.

'Daddy, can Ah bring Brendan Diamond in?'

'Aye, surely, son.'

And the three of us sat there, nibbling at my Da's Wagon Wheel, while he showed us where our new classrooms would be on the blue-inked plans. And I couldn't stop smiling because I was getting a treat and

Brendan was getting a treat thanks to me, and all the boys on the other side of the window were saying, 'Please, Miss, can we go in too?'

Mrs Boyle was all right to me, but then I never gave her any trouble. Not like Fergal Cassidy. Do this, she'd say, do that. And he'd stamp his feet and get red in the face and say, 'I am't. I am't.' I don't know where he got that from; nobody else ever said no that way. And she'd shake her candyfloss head at him and go running for Bob Storey, and Fergal would get dragged out of the room by the ear and whacked a few times with that cane that looked like a brigadier's stick.

But even Fergal was well behaved in nature study. We all loved the sad story about the brave salmon that swam halfway round the world and then came home to spawn and die. But we weren't so keen on the cuckoo.

'The cuckoo's a bird that comes to us in spring and stays for the summer,' said Mrs Boyle. 'Do you think he likes the winter in Portstewart?'

'No, Miss,' we chorused.

'Why not?'

''Cause it's cold and it rains all the time.'

'Right. So he flies where it's warmer – to the south. Where do you think he goes?'

'To Dublin, Miss?' said somebody.

'No, even farther south than that. He goes to Africa. See here, on the map.' And she stepped over to where it hung on the wall and made wings of her hands and flapped them down the map from Ireland to the big triangle that was Africa. 'Your brother's in Africa, isn't he, Seamus? Out there telling all the little black boys and girls about God and the Catholic Church.' Seamus loved that.

'Now, the cuckoo is not a very nice bird,' Mrs Boyle continued. 'In fact, it's the laaaz–iest bird in the world. Doesn't do anything for itself. Instead of doing what the other birds do – going out and collecting twigs and leaves and building a nest – it lays its eggs in the nest of another bird. Then, when the young cuckoos hatch, do you know what they do? They push out any other eggs or baby birds they find, just *shove* them out of the nest, and they take it over. Isn't that awful?'

'Yes, Miss,' we said, horrified at the wickedness of it.

Mrs Boyle told us a lot more about the cuckoo. It usually flew on its own, though you might sometimes see a male flapping about loudly after a female. It liked woods and farmland, and sand dunes like the ones behind the Strand. It could eat the fat, orange, woolly caterpillars that Paul Gray and I sometimes found at the edge of the playground, the sort of caterpillars that would poison other birds, because it had a protective stomach that it could shed and renew.

It's funny how all that's stayed with me and I haven't looked at a bird book for years. But I think I know why: it's because the cuckoo comes in summer, and it takes over somebody else's home.

Seven

I suppose it was the cuckoos in our house that turned me into a reader. For that's what I am: the reader, the bookworm. Just as Sean is the practical one like my Da, and Anne's the one everyone says is most like my Ma, and Roisin's the rebel. That's the theory about big families, isn't it? You become a somebody, a something, to make sure you stand out from the rest and don't get forgotten. Some of us work at it, some of us are given labels and live up to them, and some of us are naturals. Roisin was a natural. The rows she and my Da used to have over make-up and clothes! It was the mustard leather hotpants that really set him off.

'Where do ye think you're goin'?'

'Down the street.'

'Not dressed like that, ye're not.'

'Och, Daddy.'

'Don't you "Och, Daddy" me. Get upstairs and get somethin' dacent on. And while ye're at it get that muck off yer face. Ye look like a – '

'Like a what?'

'Never you mind. Just get up them stairs and get changed.'

And now look at her: a homebody in Hicksville, New South Wales, with husband and kids. The school run, the washing, the ironing, the dusting. Broken Hill. It doesn't sound like a place of fresh starts; it sounds more like a pile of false ones. But that's not the way Vincent saw it. He'd been there before, could get a job again, and without going through the religion-guessing interviews you have to put up with here. Their kids would thrive in the heat and the sun and grow up big and strong. Like himself. He's an unlikely mate for Roisin after all those flash gits she used to see; red-faced and roly-poly, full of fun. 'Who's that?' my Ma used to squeal when he came up behind her and tickled her in the kitchen. 'It's me – the Bad Egg.' I'd have put money on Roisin ending up with a baddie, but never with a Bad Egg.

She was a rebel from as early as I remember, probably had it stamped over her birthday suit. But I came to the books in a roundabout way. When I first hid behind the settee it was to get away from the Daleks. They were attacking Dr Who, gliding after him down a long grey corridor. He tried door after door and found every one locked, and all the time they were gaining on him, those giant pepperpots on wheels, swivelling their tops, firing blasts from their stick guns, threatening in tinny voices to '*Ex–ter–mi–nate, Ex–ter–mi–nate, Ex–ter–mi–nate*'. They scared the shit out of me. If I'd watched for a few minutes longer, of course, I'd have seen the good doctor, scarf flying behind him, slam the door of his Tardis with seconds to spare. But I didn't. I got in behind the settee.

But it wasn't fear that made me keep going back – it was the chance to get a few minutes' peace. I'd found a place of my own. There was no danger of my Ma, once I'd got cosy, coming along and telling me to get up and make room for Davy or Miss Lambert, the way she always did just when I'd got settled in an armchair. Much as I loved the pair of them, I didn't see why they should always have the best seats in the house.

I got a right crack on the head that second or third time I went in because I forgot about the bloody washhand basin and tried to straighten up. It wouldn't have happened in a normal house; people who don't keep boarders don't have any need for a washhand basin in their living room. But it was fine if I went in feet first, shuffled along and lay on my stomach. The angle of the settee's back against the wall made it feel like I was in a tent. A tent with room for only one.

I pitched that tent on sites all over the world, and it was *Hutchinson's Twentieth-Century Encyclopedia* that took me to them. It was lying on the floor under the window that day when I slid behind the settee. I'd seen Patricia and Bredge dipping into it now and again when they were doing their homework, but I don't think I'd ever looked at it before. The glossy dust jacket had long since fallen to bits and the plain wine-coloured cover wasn't exactly a come-on. I think it was the smell of the creamy pages I liked: dry and smoky like the butts my Da left overnight in the ashtray. After I'd had a good sniff I started flicking through it. Flags of the world in colour at the front, maps of the world in colour at the back. All the other drawings and photographs were in black and white, some of them no bigger than stamps, but they were enough to draw me into the words. I started reading, dipping in and out, moving from A to Z and back again. I remember being pissed off that Limavady wasn't listed – how could they have left out the town where Granny and Aunt Sally lived? – but on the page where it should have been I discovered that LIMA was the capital of Peru and that LILY-OF-THE-VALLEY wasn't just my Ma's perfume but a plant too. I was hooked. Dr Who could keep his bloody Tardis; I preferred the encyclopedia.

My Ma's always saying she had trouble getting it off me when somebody else wanted to use it. It might have been bought for the whole family (or handed down to us, more likely), but I started to carry it around with me everywhere as if it was mine, driving the rest of them mad by playing the quizmaster. I can imagine...

'How big is a proper football pitch, Daddy?'

'Ah dunno, son. How big is it?'

'At least a hundred yards long and fifty yards wide.'

'How do you begin a letter to the Pope, Roisin?'

'How would I know? *I'm* not in the habit o' writin' tae 'im.'

'Your Holiness...'

But the best one, my Ma says, was when I accused her of trying to murder the whole family as she was ladling out the pudding. It said in the encyclopedia that tapioca contained a poisonous juice; was she absolutely sure she'd got it all out? God, I must have been a right wee pain in the arse...

Then there was Bobby Brewster and the sardines. I loved those Bobby Brewster stories. The pages were nearly as stiff as cardboard, so there weren't many of them. I'd race through them and as soon as I'd finished go back and read them all over again. Bobby played conkers with a conker that talked... Bobby stood on a piece of crazy paving that laughed... Bobby heard an echo that had hiccups... And the only thing that made him different from Michael Kerr was that he ate sardine sandwiches.

I must have pestered my Ma for three or four days for sardines.

'Ye won't like them.'

'Ah will.'

'What put the idea o' them in yer head anyway?'

'There's a boy at school says they're lovely.'

And then finally I came home that day and she dished them up on a slice of toast.

'Yeugh! Goldfish!' Sean said.

My Ma told him what they were, said he could have a taste, too, if he liked.

'No, thanks,' he said, screwing up his nose.

My plate was at this end of the table. My Ma sat down with a mug of tea at that end. Sean was right. Under the blanket of orangey sauce they did look like goldfish, so I scraped that to the edge of the plate. I cut one in half, slicing off a sliver of toast with it, and put it in my mouth. They didn't feel right together, the warm toast and the cold fish. Then I bit into them. It was bloody horrible. It put me in mind of cod-liver oil. (It still does, even now. When I taste a sardine I think of standing by the pull-down cupboard before going off to school in the morning and having my Ma spoon the cod-liver oil into me. Codliv'roil, we used to say, getting the syllables over with as quickly as the tonic.)

I could feel the table shaking with my Ma's effort to hold in the giggles.

'D'ye not like them?' she said eventually.

I told her they were all right, but that I wouldn't want to be eating too many of them. I forced the rest of the sardine down and began sawing a tiny piece from another one. That's when she put me out of my misery. Grabbing the knife and fork with one hand, she whisked the plate away with the other. 'Maybe yer Daddy'll have them in his sandwiches themorra,' she said. 'An' if he doesn't, there's a cat round the corner that'll be glad o' them. Now, would ye like a wee bun tae take the taste away?'

I gave up on the sardines after that, but I stuck with Bobby Brewster. I suppose that was the first time I was ever carried away by fiction. Bobby seemed as real to me then as Sean was. More real than Stephen Dedalus is now, or David Copperfield or Holden Caulfield. We were all reading the Brewster stories then, and when we'd finished the ones in school we kept on and on until Bob Storey got the mobile library to bring us more. And then he came in that day and told us that the man who'd written them was going to come and talk to us . . . Or at least he'd be coming to Preston's, and we'd be going there to hear him.

That was something in itself; not even the big boys who played Preston's at football had ever been inside the school at that stage. 'Look,' somebody said, when Bob Storey had us all lined up outside, 'they've got an upstairs.'

'It doesn't say Preston's on the front, so why's it called Preston's?' somebody else whispered.

''Cause the headmaster is Mr Preston.'

'Then why isn't ours called Storey's instead of St Colum's?'

''Cause it's named after a saint, an' saints are more important than headmasters.'

They had a hall, which was another thing we didn't have. 'Ye could play five-a-sides in here,' said Eamonn O'Rourke, and you could have done if half the floor hadn't been covered with chairs. Preston's filled most of them, but they'd left a section for us at the front, and Mrs Boyle and Mrs McGurk shooed us into it. Bob Storey stood at the back, chatting to another man. 'That's Mr Preston,' somebody said, and we all turned to look.

He was a giant. When Bob Storey stood at his side he looked like a wee boy admiring a soldier in a sentry box.

H. E. Todd wasn't so big. About the same height as Bob, but without the dandruff on the shoulders. I recognized him immediately because he looked just like the photo on his books. When he came up to the front and the clapping died down and he began to read, I looked at the clock above his head. It was a quarter to twelve. I wondered whether he'd be able to read a whole story before we had to stop for the Angelus. Mrs McGurk was strict about that. 'I don't care *how* near you are to finishing. It's twelve noon. It's time for the Angelus, so put your pens down.' And up we would get and start to pray: 'The Angel of the Lord appeared unto Mary, and she conceived by the Holy Ghost. Hail Mary, full of grace...'

I'd always thought of Bobby Brewster as just a boy. It wasn't until H. E. Todd started to read in an English accent that I realized he was an *English* boy. But I still liked him, and I liked H. E. Todd. He wasn't a bit like those English people who'd made Judette cry.

When I noticed the clock next it was ten to one. The last story had just finished. Everybody was clapping, even Mrs McGurk, who seemed to have completely forgotten about the Angelus. She was standing by the gate as we filed out and I stopped to ask her why we hadn't said it. As soon as the words were out of my mouth I realized I knew the answer, but Eamonn O'Rourke was right behind me and ready with it anyway. 'Are you stupid or somethin'?' he said. 'It's because we're in a school for Prodesans. Isn't that right, Miss?'

The story I liked best that day was the one about Bobby Brewster and the genie. Bobby's staying with his mother and father in a hotel and the manager says that as a special treat he can bang the gong before dinner. Bobby's practising for this when the genie appears. He's only a trainee genie so he can't conjure piles of gold coins or palaces or beautiful princesses, but he does have a few tricks. One of them is to make sure that what leaves the kitchen as a plate of chicken turns into a plate of sardines by the time it reaches Bobby Brewster.

H. E. Todd has a lot to answer for. It's his fault I wasted all that time trying to summon the genie on our own gong. I couldn't wait to get home and try it. I thought the genie might be able to magic me now and again to Limavady, so that instead of living in a boarding house I could live at the back of Aunt Sally's sweet shop. If he turned out to be a trainee, and that was beyond his powers, at least he'd be good company in the tent, and if he got too big for that I could put him back in his bottle.

I couldn't reach the gong then as easily as I can now. I had to drag a chair from the dining room into the hall and stand on it. I banged it softly at first, partly because that was what Bobby had done and partly because I didn't want anybody in the kitchen to hear. Genies must have good hearing, so there was no need to bang too hard. I waited for ages, but there was no response. I tried again, a bit louder. Still nothing. The next time I walloped it. Bong! Bong! Bong!

For a minute nothing happened. Then the door of the kitchen flew open and Anne came running out. 'Michael! What d'ye think ye're playin' at? Put that gong away and get down before ye fall. It's only four o'clock and ye'll have everybody in the house in the dinin' room lookin' for their tea.'

I tried again the next day, muttering the odd abracadabra just to help things along. Still nothing.

The last go was on a lovely sunny day. The light coming through the side panels by the door put a sparkle on the gong and the bracket. I thought it was a magic light. I tried a couple of gentle strikes, and waited a good minute. No response. I banged again, a bit harder this time, and the gong vibrated for a few seconds, sending rays of light skittering all over the wall. I leaned closer to watch it, to see the last of the tiny movements die away.

And then I heard the scrape of a foot in the porch and a heavy knock on the door. I nearly fell off the chair. I wanted a genie, not a giant in hobnail boots. And weren't they supposed to materialize beside you instead of banging on doors? There I was, turned to jelly on the chair, when there was another knock, and a voice shouted out: 'Mrs Kerr, are ye there? Ah've got yer mince.' Then the door opened and John Lyons stuck his head round it. He looked at me, drumstick shaking in my hand, and winked. 'Is it teatime already, son?' he said.

Eight

God, I'm hungry. A couple of slices of toast would do. I
wonder what's in the bread bin. The wheaten looks a bit
hard – somebody's forgotten to wrap it up again – but
there's a couple of heels in this Mother's Pride bag. Best
bit o' the loaf, my Da says. But then he says that the rind
is the best bit of the bacon and that the fat's the best bit
of a pork chop. It's no wonder his arteries are clogged.

But I do like heels. I couldn't believe it when Mrs
Sullivan was making toast for breakfast and she opened
the loaf, put one of her dainty feet on the pedal of the
bin and flicked the heel straight into it. 'That's my
favourite bit,' I wanted to say, but I couldn't. I didn't want
her to take me for a culchie. She'd have been writing
back to Maisie saying that young Michael was very well
mannered when he was over but we did have to keep
him from eating the scraps.

I moan like hell about Maisie, but if it hadn't been for her I wouldn't have had the Sullivans to stay with. I'd have been finding my way round London and getting to the interview at the college all on my own. 'Isn't he a lovely fella, my Tom?' she said when I got back, as if he was her own son instead of somebody she nursed when he was a wean. And he is a lovely man. I liked his wife, too. Classy. Not sexy classy – she was too mousey for that – but polished. How could I have bought her that bloody cannon? How could I have been so stupid? It was all the silver she had in the cabinet. I thought of that when I was in the department store and it seemed right to buy her another bit. But why didn't I get her a candlestick or a vase or a picture frame? She's probably sitting there laughing about it now with Tom, asking what is she supposed to do with a silver cannon, and why are the Irish so obsessed with guns. 'Ah hope ye got her some flowers or somethin' for puttin' ye up,' my Ma said when I got back. And I hadn't even thought of them till then. Flowers. Of course. Of bloody course.

She had them all round the house, great big bunches of lilies, and the couple of evenings I was there she was in the garden cutting more. It was a big garden, but the house was smaller than I expected. When Maisie said he'd been in charge of the Metropolitan Police traffic department I thought it would be a lot grander. And I thought he would have had a newer car, too, something shiny and slick instead of that old Rover. Still, it did the job.

He'd warned me that the Elephant and Castle wasn't the prettiest part of town, but when he dropped me off there in the morning I could have got straight back in the car and straight back on the plane. The world's biggest bloody traffic island, surrounded by tower blocks and with that shopping centre the colour of bubble gum. It's hardly surprising the subways are full of men on meths; if I had to live there I'd want to blot it all out too. But, as Dick keeps telling me, I don't have to live there. I'll only be going to college there five days a week, and the rest of the time I'll be able to enjoy the pubs and the clubs and the galleries and all the rest of it. Or as much of the rest of it as the grant will buy.

When Tom said he wouldn't be able to take me there *and* back, and asked me if I'd be all right coming back to Kingston on the Underground and the train, I was thinking, Oh, no, I'm gonna get lost. But I couldn't have told him, any more than I could have told that air hostess on the way over that I didn't know how to fasten the seatbelt. I'm sure she noticed, though; she was looking straight at me during the demonstration, probably because I was the only one looking at her, and she kept giving me wee smiles after that.

Anyway, I'd already felt green enough admitting it was my first time in London and my first flight anywhere. I couldn't tell him I'd never been on a train before. Thank God he wrote it all down for me. Northern Line from Elephant and Castle to Balham, then British Rail from there to Clapham Junction and on to Kingston. I looked at that note so many times I can still recite it. 'It's very straightforward,' he said. 'When you get to Kingston, just give me a ring and I'll come and meet you.'

It was straightforward, too – well, once I'd got on the train. The doors would have closed on me if that big guy inside hadn't forced them apart again. Then he and everybody else sat down and hid behind their papers. They all knew where they were going but I was staring hard through the windows to make sure I didn't miss my stop.

Reading all the ads, too. There was even one about suspicious packages and what to do if you saw one. I'd been looking at the ad for Kelly Girls and I was thinking about Patricia Kelly from school, and then about the girls and how they could have found jobs in London without going all the way to Australia, when I saw the box.

We'd gone – what? – five stops by then. I suppose nobody else had seen it because they were all reading. It was on the last seat, by the door, at the end of the carriage. 'Kerrygold Butter' it said on the side. I thought, If you were going to put a bomb on a train you wouldn't put it in a box that had held Irish butter, would you? And then I thought, Maybe you would as a sort of double-bluff. The notice said that if you saw a suspicious package you should pull the emergency handle when the train got into the next station and tell the guard. I thought of doing that. And then I thought that when they heard my accent they'd jump to conclusions. Even just sitting there I felt as though there was an invisible cord tying me and the box together. So I didn't do a thing.

When we pulled into the next station I saw a couple who got on look at the box and then look away. I thought of getting off and waiting for another train, but I didn't know how frequent they were and I was worried about missing the connection at Clapham Junction and having Tom Sullivan worrying about me. So I stayed on. Then Colonel Blimp came striding up from the other end of the carriage in his pinstripes. I suppose he'd looked up from his paper, noticed the package and taken it upon himself to do something about it. 'Is that yours?' he began asking everybody, and they all put down their papers and books and looked at the box. 'Is that yours?' No, they all said. I just shook my head, but when he looked straight at me with those grey eyes I thought he'd be able to tell I was Irish anyway. He asked if anybody knew how long it had been sitting there, and I shook my head again. And then at the next station he pulled the emergency handle.

The whole place went mad. Men in uniform running up and down asking who'd pulled the handle. Colonel Blimp waving them up to our carriage. Somebody shouting 'Everybody off, *now!*' and, 'Don't board this train.' And I was thinking of what I'd been saying only an hour earlier at the interview, about having grown up in a part of Northern Ireland that didn't have bomb scares, and now here I was in London in the middle of one.

We all hovered for a while like people at a road accident, hoping to see something but ready to speed on if it proved too strong. Then a guard came up and Colonel Blimp pointed to the box and the guard got on the train. He went straight over to the box and prodded it with his finger. We all turned away then – pointlessly, because if it had gone off we'd have been blown to smithereens. 'It's soft,' the guard said. 'It *must* be butter.' And I was thinking, Has the man never heard of plastic explosives? As if I was any better placed than he was to know what they felt like.

It was then I looked behind me and saw Balham on the sign and realized that I'd gone as far as I needed to anyway. So I left them to it and went up the escalator. And all the way up I was expecting to hear a bang.

If I told my Ma this she'd say, 'Well, why didn't *you* pull the emergency handle when you were the one who saw it first? It might have been a real bomb. Ye might have been killed along with everybody else.' And what would I tell her? That I was sure they'd see the invisible cord that tied me to the box? That I was scared the police would lift me because of the way I talked? 'Och, Michael,' she'd say. 'Ah thought ye had more sense.'

Something's burning... Shit! The toast! Black as the road. Ah, well, it'll have to be the wheaten after all. My Ma'll be keeping that other bread for the visitors' breakfast. Just as well I didn't bring Dick back with me – I might have ended up doing a five-loaves-and-two-fishes job.

He found it really funny the first time he came in here.

'So you've got a range in the kitchen...'

'Yeah.'

'... *and* a gas cooker...'

'Yeah.'

'... and an electric cooker in the scullery.'

I suppose it is a bit odd if you're not used to it; if you don't know what it's like at the height of summer before dinner with pots and pans having to be bubbling away everywhere at the same time.

God knows what we're still doing with so many pots and pans, not to mention soup plates and pudding bowls and dinner plates. And when was the last time anybody in this house used a fish-knife? We could manage with the half of it now we're just doing bed and breakfast. The shelves are sagging and those dovetails of my Da's are only just holding the drawers together. Mention having a clear-out and my Ma says, 'Aye, surely – an' in the summer we'll find oursel's short.'

The only thing we've ever been short of in the summer is places to sleep, and things haven't improved greatly even since my Da built the back house. The definition in that dictionary of Northern Ireland dialect in the library suggests some giant extension, a sort of second house at the back of the first that the family retreats to to make way for the paying guests. Huh! I wish ours had been that size.

It looks big enough now, when it's just a store for tools and off-cuts of timber and fishing rods and junk, but it was different then. The bunk beds behind the door, two double beds jammed together along the wall on the left, a mattress under the window, a wardrobe along the far wall, and so many cardboard boxes full of clothes and shoes and toys and books that you were cursing and swearing from barking your shins every time you got up in the dark to go to the loo.

'Who's makin' all that racket?' my Da would shout from the kitchen, his temper not improved by the prospect of spreading a mattress on the tiles. And a few minutes later he'd be snoring for Ireland, my Ma nudging him this way and that in an effort to shut him up long enough so she could fall asleep herself. And no sooner would she have done that than it was time to be up and about lighting fires and restarting the cycle of breakfast and dinner and tea and supper.

How did she do it? How did *we* do it?

As soon as the breakfast dishes were washed and dried, Sean and I'd be bashing the spuds, one with a knife at the sink, the other in the yard twisting the knob on that big cylindrical peeler with the surface inside like a cheese grater's. God, that made your wrists ache! And even when you'd finished you still had to go over them all by hand to take the eyes out.

Meanwhile, the girls would be making the beds and dusting and polishing and setting the table for dinner. Another flurry of serving and washing-up and then we'd escape to the Harbour Hill or the Herring Pond or the flat roof with a good book until just before teatime. More serving, more washing-up.

Then, when the girls were summoning the energy to go out to a dance and we boys were heading out again to the Harbour Hill, my Ma and Da were still hard at it. There was porridge to be boiled, bacon to be rinded. Why the hell did we do that? Why did my Da sit there cutting the rind off slice by slice with a pair of scissors? Was it to make the streaky less streaky-looking, a bit more meaty and appetizing? If we'd bought back bacon he could have saved himself a lot of bother; and we *could* have bought back if we'd charged a bit more.

Look at this copy of the bill my Ma gave those Russians when they were here. When was that? 1973 it says here. (They looked so exotic, the signatures they left in the visitors' book; all those CCCPs coming after the Bangors and the Belfasts and the Omaghs. Nearly as exotic as that foxy blonde intepreter they had with them. What was she called? Diana. It would have been worth putting up with the bread queues just to move to Moscow with her.)

Look what my Ma charged them:

Bed and breakfast for 11 people for four days @ £1.50 each	£66
Evening four-course dinner for 11 people for four days @ £1.25 each	£55
Packed lunches for 11 people for two days @ 75p each	£16.50

And that was three years ago. And all her costs have risen since then and she's still charging £1.50 for bed and breakfast and £1.25 for dinner. I'm no economist, but even I can see that you're not going to make a decent living if you do that.

My Da doesn't help, the way he carries on. The girls finally persuade my Ma that it just doesn't make sense any more to serve suppers, so what does he do? He gets into the habit of having a drink with half a dozen of the visitors in the pub and then inviting them all back to the kitchen. 'Morelli's? Ye've no need tae be goin' down to Morelli's and spendin' money hand over fist. Sure come back wi' me and we'll get ye a sandwich or two in the kitchen.'

So when we were all looking to wind down and collapse into bed we'd find ourselves being called on to butter bread and cut cake and apologize for having no mustard left to put in the ham sandwiches. And then my Da would get the fiddle out and we'd have to bloody well sing for them as well.

'Great crack, yer Da,' Dick says, and he can be, but there were nights when he had the rest of us wishing he'd take his party somewhere else.

Dick's house is like a library in comparison – only the four of them there now that his sister's in Milton Keynes, all of them padding about in their slippers. I used to think they were posher than us because they wore slippers, even though they live in a council house and we have our own place. My Ma and Da are still the only ones in our house who wear them. That time I suggested she buy me a pair in Coleraine my Ma thought it was a great laugh. 'An' a pipe as well, Ah suppose? Then ye'll have all ye need tae retire before ye've left school.'

'But Ah want tae save mae shoes by not wearin' them roun' the house more than Ah need to.'

'Ye can save yer shoes a whole lot better by not kickin'' football in them.'

Dick's Da has some connection with Belfast Celtic. Maybe he even played for them, but that would have been a long time ago. Nowadays he's as fond of the whiskey as my Da, except he drinks Jamieson's rather than Bush. Dick reckons he gets through a bottle a day in instalments – a quick one every time he nips across the road from the bookie's to watch the races. What was it he said to my Da the day after they first met? 'Forgotten mae name already, have ye? It's John Kennedy. But ye might remember it better if it was John Jamieson.'

He'd enjoy a drop of what's down here behind the bread bin. 'Cantrell & Cochrane, Ice-cream Soda' it says on the label. But the label's a lie. This stuff's as clear as soda, all right, but it won't fizz if you shake it. It wouldn't be poteen if it did.

Pot–yeen.

The first time I heard the word was when I asked my Da whether I could have a drop of his lemonade. He laughed and told me it was the sort of lemonade that would make a wee boy very sick.

'Make ye blind, more like,' my Ma said.

'It's poteen,' he said. 'It's what they call mountain dew, cause it's made by very clever men in the mountains.'

'Huh,' my Ma said, with a sour face.

Where in the mountains, I wanted to know.

'Never you mind where.'

The only mountain I knew of was the one on the way to Granny's, so I guessed the poteen came from some-where near there. A while later, when I'd learned that poteen-making was against the law, I pictured the man who made it in a log cabin deep in the conifers of Springwell Forest. He'd be scrawny, long-bearded and in dungarees, like one of the *Beverly Hillbillies* but a damn sight smarter. He'd have to be, to outwit the police and the customs men. He'd be bent over some Heath Robinson arrangement of pipes and tubes and flasks, and he'd watch this evil liquid bubble and steam and fart from one end of it to the other, and then he'd bottle it, giggling to himself at the ice-cream-soda labels. Then it would be packed in secret compartments in cars or lorries, and passed from hand to hand under tables in pubs, finally reaching my Da and getting hidden away behind the big green enamel bread bin.

Until my Ma got her hands on it. I remember that first time she watered it down. My Da's car had hardly disappeared before she was racing to the scullery to pull the bottle from its hiding place. Sean and I were following her. 'This oul' stuff,' she said, brandishing the bottle in front of us. 'If you pair o' boys is wise ye'll never let a drop o' it past yer lips. D'ye hear me? I've known fellas in Garvagh have one wee glass o' this an' end up in a coffin.'

We watched as she spun the tap, leaving it running into the sink. Then she tipped up the bottle, poured two-thirds away, and topped it up again with tap water.

'There. Just as much as 'e had before. But this way it'll do 'im a damn sight less harm, won't it? Now, would ye like a wee biscuit? And not a word o' this tae yer Daddy when 'e gets home, d'ye hear?'

Nine

There's no smell to it, really, not even when it's right under your nose. A hint of spuds going off, maybe, but that's all. You'd think firewater would stink, wouldn't you? But it doesn't. Not like the Bush on my Da's breath when he gets back from the Splash – that would put you out. And to think that he used to dip the teat of my bottle in it when I was teething to help me get over to sleep... Or so he says. I wouldn't put it past him. Maybe that's why I hate it so much. Well, that and my Ma wincing every time she sees the bottle. 'That oul' stuff. It turns mae stomach just tae look at it.' It must have been awful for her on those evenings when everybody else was sitting round the fire getting pissed and she spent four hours nursing one Babycham. But she did enjoy the music; we all did.

I used to love it when the girls' singing woke me up;

those harmonies they did on 'Ebony Eyes' and 'Banks of the Ohio'. I'd want to turn the volume up, and the only way to do that was to creep down the stairs and sit on the step opposite the breakfast-room door. It was freezing there, the draught from the front door making flags of my pyjama legs. But I'd sit for ages.

My Da came out that night to go into the kitchen. The juddering of the breakfast-room door had warned me, and I'd raced up the stairs, but he still heard me. 'Who's that out o' bed? Is that you, Michael?'

I said it was.

'Did ye think ye were missin' somethin'? Do ye want tae come down for a wee singsong? Come on.'

So I went back down and he put his big hand on my shoulder and steered me through the doorway. 'Here's another fella might do a turn for us,' he said.

The room was thick with cigarette smoke. Mary McNally was on the settee in the corner nearest the fire, her face as red as the coals. My Ma was in the middle, Trish at the other end. Roisin sat with her legs dangling sideways over one armchair, Anne in another one. Bredge squatted like a tailor on the floor. They were all turned towards the wall to the right of the door, where three of the bentwood chairs were drawn up. My Da's mandolin rested against one of the chairs. Peter McNally, wiping Guinness froth from his fleshy lips with one hand, lifted a fiddle with the other. Farthest from the door was Frank Doherty, in grey beard and Aran jumper, like a sailor home from the sea. All around them on the floor were ashtrays and Guinness bottles and half-empty beer glasses and tumblers of whiskey.

'Would ye look at the size o' him!' said Mary, rising

from her seat. 'Which one's this? Michael? Come over here till Ah see ye. Would ye like a wee biscuit?'

She reached for a marshmallow from the tray on the floor and pressed it into my hand. Then she grabbed me and planted a kiss on me. She smelt of whiskey and face cream.

'That wean should be in his bed,' my Ma said. 'He has school in the mornin' and he'll be fit for nothin'.' Her glass of Babycham sat on the mantelpiece next to the bottle. It had hardly been touched.

'He'll be all right,' my Da said. 'Sure half an hour won't hurt him. Now, who's for another drink? Peter?'

He unscrewed the top of the whiskey bottle and advanced towards Peter's glass where it sat on the floor.

'Mick, no more for me,' Peter protested. But before he could move his glass away my Da had grabbed it and splashed in a top-up.

'God, Mick, but ye're a wil' man,' Peter said, shaking his head. 'I have tae drive tae Portrush, remember.'

'Sure that wee drop won't do ye any harm. Mary, come on. Ye've been nursin' that one since ye got here.'

While my Da went to the kitchen for more drinks, the girls all reached towards me, each patting her lap. I didn't know where to turn. In the end, Roisin swept me on to her knee. 'Come on up here till I get a cuddle.'

My Da came back with a six-pack of dumpy bottles of Guinness and shared it with the other men. I watched Frank pour one, his hand shaking as he held the glass almost horizontal. A few drops fell to the floor. He looked up, guiltily, to see if anyone had noticed. Only me. He winked at me.

My Da lifted his mandolin, set it down against the wall

and picked up his fiddle. Sitting down, he ran the bow across the strings and launched straight into a jig.

It was a tune he's played hundreds of times and I still don't know what it's called; he and Peter used to play it every time they got together. Peter took it up on the fiddle and Frank on the tin whistle. Roisin bounced me up and down on her knee. The rest tapped feet, armrests and tables – even my Ma, though she tapped as delicately as she drank – until it seemed that the whole room was vibrating. And then, with a great 'Hey!' and a flourish like a sword cut, my Da brought the thing to an end.

He put down the fiddle and picked up the mandolin again. 'Here's one for the wee fella,' he said.

Patricia looked at me and smiled and started to sing, beckoning me over. I slid from Roisin's knee and went over to stand by the settee. Patricia had taught me the song, and how to sing it in a way that mimicked the instrument. Now we sang it together:

> *I yululused to playlaylay my ololol banjololo*
> *And nurlurlus it ololon my kneeleelee.*
> *But nowlowlow the strililings are brololoken*
> *   dowlowlown*
> *And nololo more yululuse to meleelee . . .*

When I finished, Trish made me give them a bow, and they all clapped.

'Now,' Frank said, 'who's for "The Sash"?' He started playing it straight away on his tin whistle. My Da and Peter and a couple of the girls started singing:

> *It was old and it was beautiful*

And the colours they were fine.
It was worn at Derry, Aughrim,
Enniskillen and the Boyne . . .

That must have been the first time I heard 'The Sash' in our house. I knew I'd heard it before, but it took me a minute or two to remember where. It was the one the Orangemen played as they paraded down the Prom in the summer. The first couple of times I'd heard it, banged out on those giant drums, it had scared the life out of me. I wasn't scared this time, but I was puzzled. Why, I wondered, were we singing about 'the sash my father wore' when it was only Protestants who wore sashes?

After the second chorus, Frank got up, still playing, and began to march round the room as if he was an Orangeman. He was going round the edge of the hearth and past my Ma when he tripped on the rug, fell over on her, and nearly knocked the glass out of her hand.

'Ah'm sorry, Mrs Kerr,' he said, picking himself up. 'Ah doubt Ah've overdone it a wee bit.'

'Ye could hardly help it, Frank,' she said, 'the way that man's throwin' drink at ye.' She looked at my Da, but he was avoiding her eye.

'Are ye all right?' Frank asked.

'Aye,' she said, 'no damage done, but maybe you'd be safer sittin' down.'

Frank nodded, stumbled back to his chair and took up on the whistle again. My Da and Peter sang on till the end; on their own until the final, resounding chorus, when the girls all joined in.

There was a pause. Mary excused herself and I heard her footsteps going up towards the toilet. Instruments were downed, glasses raised – apart from Frank's. He looked longingly at his, then over at my Ma, but didn't touch it.

'One from our own side, now,' Peter said, and he picked up his fiddle and started to play. Everybody but my Ma began to sing:

> *Oh, we're all off to Dublin in the green in the green*
> *With the helmets glistenin' in the sun.*
> *And we're off to join the IRA*
> *And we're off tomorrow morn...*

'The Soldier's Song'. It's a long time since we've sung that. Funny how everybody knew fewer verses of it than they did of 'The Sash'. It was a folk song in those days, a bit of history, and then the Troubles started and it became a political song again, a dangerous song. Singing it suggested you supported the IRA. I don't think there was any discussion among my Da and the rest of them – not that I'd have been old enough to be privy to it, anyway – I think it just got quietly dropped from the repertoire.

Or maybe my Ma told them to drop it. She didn't like it even in those days. She'd be sitting on eggs when they were singing it, pointing at the back wall and waving her hand the way she did when she wanted the volume on the TV turned down. I remember her telling me that when we were small my Da would play one night in a Catholic church hall and the next night in a Protestant hall; that he enjoyed one just as much as the other. That's what she told me that first time when I asked her why we'd been singing 'The Sash' when it was a Protestant song. 'Protestant or Catholic, Orange or Green, we make no difference,' she said. But we did. I knew even then that we did. Because I was cute.

I wonder how many times I pinched a bun or a biscuit when I was a wean and thought I'd got clean away with it, and then heard my Ma coming up behind me to tell me I was 'far too cute'... They didn't understand the word when I used it that way in London. When I talked about children growing cute fast they thought I meant cuddly cute. I had to spell it out for them: crafty, wily, quick on the uptake. You learn that your elders talk in code, and that while some phrases are spoken softly they're loud with a double meaning.

I suppose the first time it clicked with me was that night Joe Campbell came round to see my Da. He had some plastering that needed doing. My Da wasn't home yet.

'Sure sit an' wait for him,' my Ma said, pulling chairs nearer the heat of the range. 'He'll only be half an hour. I was just makin' a drap o' tay, anyway.'

'Naw, not for me, Annie. I've just risen from tay at home.'

'Sure a wee cup in yer han' won't do ye any harm. Bredge, love, will ye go and get a few biscuits?'

My Ma made the tea. Bredge passed round the biscuits. Joe congratulated Bredge and me on how fast we were growing, as if we'd put on another couple of inches since yesterday.

'Anythin' startlin', Annie?' Joe asked.

'Oh, nothin' pass-remarkable.'

For a few minutes there was talk of the weather and how hard it was to find a decent floury spud these days and the quare turnout there had been for Barney the

Rogue's funeral, God rest him. Then, as the tea was topped up and the biscuits went around again, Joe started talking about my Da.

'So, Mick's in Coleraine, now...'

'Aye,' my Ma said. 'Started on Friday last an' I hope it'll keep him goin' for a wee while yet. It's the Bull's Eye they're at, ye know.'

'Ah've not been in that place in years,' Joe said. 'But Ah know from the outside o' it it's badly in need o' a lick o' paint. Yer man McNulty has it now, hasn't he? He's doin' rightly for himsel'. Do ye know is he from our side of the house...?'

There it was. That phrase I was always hearing; that phrase I'm *still* always hearing. Is he from our side of the house? Is he Catholic?

'Is it true that you lot can always tell who's Protestant and who's Catholic?' that guy Simon asked me at the college. And I told him how we do it – how the school's a giveaway and you can make a good guess from the name or the place they work or the town. But I forgot to mention the intelligence you can gather in kitchens. I suppose we take it for granted. But he'd enjoy it. It tells you so much about the way we think, doesn't it?

Somebody new moves into a pub or a boarding house or takes over as a dentist or doctor. My Ma and Da and the aunts and uncles sit here round the range weighing him up. Is he a good-lookin' fella or like the back-end of a bus? Is he tight or generous? Is he a smart boy or did he come up the Bann on a bubble? (I love that phrase, that notion of a character who's so frothy he just blows up the river with the spume.)

Eventually, after a bit of side-stepping, somebody gets

to the point. The voice drops, as if whoever's asking is embarrassed, or worried that the walls have ears, or both. And then we hear: 'Is he from our side o' the house, do ye know?'

'Ye may be sure he's not.'

'Damn the bit of 'im. There's no chance for any o' ours in there.'

And there's that clicking of the tongue against the roof of the mouth, or a tight pursing of the lips and a resigned shake of the head.

But just now and again the answer's yes. Somebody's seen this new guy at Mass or the sister of a teacher says he's been in to look round St Colum's with his kids. And then, especially if his job's a good one, a well-paid one, it's all smiles and congratulations, as if he's done something for all of us. 'Good man. Isn't that great tae see? All credit tae 'im.'

They usually guess right, too. You're one side of the house or the other, and whichever it is everybody soon gets to hear. Everybody but the weans, who aren't supposed to know what you're talking about at all. And whenever they come running in you've got to remind everybody to guard their tongues, because you don't want this sort of talk repeated on the Harbour Hill, do you? 'Whatever ye say, say nothin'.'

How long was it before I realized that that phrase had a second meaning; that it was a worn piece of advice? Somebody on our side of the house who felt himself wronged by somebody on the other would be reminded that he was in the minority; that it would do no good to kick up a fuss; that he would just have to live with it because this was the way things were. *Whatever ye say, say nothin'*. It's not a bit like that soppy, watery, English phrase, 'Least said, soonest mended.' It's a bitter acceptance that things are beyond mending.

Even at the age of seven or eight, I knew there were offices and factories and housing estates and whole towns where people from our side of the house weren't welcome. Nobody had told me that, but then they didn't have to. All they had to say was that such and such a place was 'a black wee hole'. I was cute enough to know what they meant.

Ten

I hadn't actually been to any of the black wee holes by then. There was the occasional trip to Coleraine to the shops, or to Limavady to see Granny and Aunt Sally. Otherwise the edges of the world were the house and the Harbour Hill and the school and the chapel.

Winnie and Peter took us a bit further afield. Sean and I were in heaven when they came over to stay. We seemed to spend every day on the beach or the Strand or darting round those rock pools behind Phillips's garage trying to catch sticklebacks. '*My*kal! *My*kal! Over here!' Winnie would shout when she spotted one. I'd never heard anyone say my name the way she did. She had an excuse: she was English. Or so we thought then – it was years before I realized she'd been born here. But I couldn't understand how my Da's brother, who'd grown up in Tyrone, sounded as if he'd spent all his life in

Yorkshire. 'Shall we go down't pond,' he'd suggest in that rumbling bass as soon as we'd got the breakfast dishes cleared away. I think he enjoyed it as much as we did.

He loved the singsongs, too, roaring away every evening on 'The Wild Rover'. Sometimes he'd lift my Da's fiddle, pluck a string or two, and then put it down with a shake of his head, as if it was beautiful but beyond him. I know the feeling – I'd love to be able to play the way the old boy does. Or the way he used to. But it's too late now to ask him...

Peter Junior was already dabbling with the tin whistle in those days. I used to think of Pan and his pipes when I saw his fingers dancing over the holes, for he looked like a Pan with that scraggy beard and rangy frame and the bright eyes. When you walked down the street with him, people behaved as if he had a tail, too, turning to look at him and his long hair and his crumpled tie-dye T-shirt and those big toes sticking out of his sandals. 'Wud ye look at the shape o' that?' you knew they were saying, and you were proud of him and embarrassed at the same time. I doubt if we'll ever see his Ma and Da again – the journey's just too much for them now. But I'm sure he'll still be popping over as the fancy takes him even when his beard's turned grey, and he'll still have no more baggage than his flute and a toothbrush, and he'll still be giving the impression that he was last in the kitchen not two years but two minutes ago.

How on earth did somebody as fussy as Winnie ever give birth to a son like him? My Ma still talks about the toilet rolls and how she couldn't understand why they were disappearing so fast that summer. And then she discovered that Winnie was putting strips of paper round the seat of the loo every time the kids went to make sure they didn't catch anything. My Ma was fit to be tied – the idea that somebody would catch germs in her toilet! But she'd never have said anything. I think she was a bit in awe of Winnie, who was always so forceful, so sure she was right.

Winnie fussed about with us too, making sure we kept on our plastic sandals in case we stepped on something sharp in the rock pools, but we did as we were told, because we knew that at the end of the day there'd be an ice-cream.

Eye-scream, wee Joe used to say it. We teased him for that, teased the life out of him when Winnie wasn't around. He was English, we'd tell him, so why couldn't he speak English? And why didn't he know that ice-cream came in a cone and not what he insisted on calling a cornet?

My Ma heard us at that one day, Adrian and Ivor and Sean and myself. She called Sean and me into the kitchen and pushed the door to.

'Ah hope ye're not bein' nasty tae wee Joe,' she said.

'No, Mammy.'

'Ah hope not. For he's yer wee cousin, remember. He's one of our own.'

And Adrian and Ivor weren't, of course. They were just neighbours. Protestant neighbours.

'So which are you,' that guy Simon said, 'Cat or Prod?' It was odd being asked that question in England; completely different from being asked it here. It was just a question, not a loaded question. It didn't matter how I answered it; it wouldn't do me any harm. For a moment

I was going to tell him to mind his own business, and then I realized why he'd asked. It was partly because he's a cocky bugger – you could see that in the way he talked to the lecturers – but it was mainly that he was curious, already playing the journalist. He really wanted to know what difference it made to your life to be one or the other. So I told him, and when he asked whether we fought with our Protestant neighbours I told him that too. Yes, we fought with our Protestant neighbours from the age of seven or eight, and our battleground was the Harbour Hill, where we dug trenches, launched charges and repelled invaders by hurling fearsomely big divots. We fought side by side, in a conflict scripted by the *Victor* and the *Hotspur*, against the Germans and the Japanese.

I suppose it was the Oul' Cook who brought us together, by giving us a common enemy. Mr Lewis of the Kinora Hotel. Well, he liked to call it a hotel, but it wasn't nearly as big then as the Sea Splash is now; it was a glorified guest house, and guest house, we knew, was just a fancy name for boarding house. So we thought he'd got a bit above himself when he started dressing in the chef's hat and checked trousers. The hat would wobble all over the place when he came out through his kitchen door to throw the ball back. Poor man . . . we must have driven him mad the number of times we kicked that ball into his yard. So we shouldn't really have been surprised when he finally flipped.

He'd just peeled his spuds and set them outside the back door in a big saucepan. Sean shot at me, I missed, the ball went sailing over the edge of the hill, hit the back door, and rebounded straight into the saucepan. A wheeker. Bobby Charlton couldn't have hit it better.

We were still marvelling at the brilliance of it when the Oul' Cook came out into the yard. He saw we were there. He knew we were waiting for him to throw the ball back. But he just stood with his feet planted a yard apart, folded his arms and glared at us.

I nudged Sean. 'You ask him,' I whispered.

'Naw. You.'

I did, eventually. 'Mr Lewis, can we have our ball back, please?'

'No,' he said in his BBC voice. 'It'll serve you right to go without it for a while. Maybe then you'll learn that you should not be playing near people's back doors.'

Then we heard another voice: 'Give the weans their ball back, ye oul' bugger.'

And there was Ian Nicholl, striding towards the edge of the hill.

'I beg your pardon,' the Oul' Cook answered. 'What did you say?'

'Ah said give the weans their ball back, ye oul' bugger.'

The Oul' Cook looked like a chef in a cartoon who's found a rat in the soup. 'How dare you talk to me like that!' he said. 'How dare you!'

Ian dared. His right arm jerked up at the elbow, he gave the Oul' Cook the fingers, and then he said: 'Away and fuck yersel!'

He didn't shout it, at least not as loudly as he might have done, but the word was still an explosion. The Oul' Cook looked as if he'd been hit by the shrapnel. He began to splutter a response, thought better of it, and went back indoors, shaking his head. Ian hawked, and spat after him. 'Miserable oul' git,' he said, and he turned, shrugged at us, and sauntered towards his own back gate.

We thought that was really something. We didn't think, 'Wait a minute, the ball's still in the yard, if Ian had been a bit more diplomatic we might have got it back.' We saw it differently. Ian was a Protestant. We were Catholics. The Oul' Cook was a Protestant, too – he must have been, for we never saw him at chapel on a Sunday. But Ian had taken our side against him.

He'd done it spectacularly, too. I spent the next few days copying him where nobody could hear me at the top of the hill, or just mouthing the word in front of the hall mirror. Front teeth pressed down on bottom lip, then the mouth flew open to free the four-letter word. F–UCK yersel'.

I imagined saying it to the Oul' Cook, and the shock there would be on his face. But I wouldn't have dared. My Da'd have hung, drawn and quartered me. He got shirty enough with Sean and me when he heard us calling each other brute and brat. The F-word was a really bad one in those days, much worse than the bloomin' and shite I was thinking of in confession when I owned up to Saying Bad Words, Telling Lies, Disobedience to My Mother and Father. We never heard it in our house, not even when my Da was drunk.

But Ian had said it, and I had heard his Da use it sometimes. It was another of the differences between Protestants and us. They went to church and we went to chapel. They called their mother Mummy and we called ours Mammy. They used the F-word and we didn't. They had better toys, too.

Those things my Da made for us – they were fine when we were pretending in the privacy of the back yard, but they were no good when we graduated to the

Harbour Hill and saw that other kids didn't have to pretend. The Nicholls didn't push a bit of wire along and tell themselves it was a bike; when they changed gear they didn't do it only in their heads. They had real bikes, two of them. Ivor had one as well. Because their parents had smaller families they could afford to buy their kids bikes. And the reason they had smaller families, I knew even then, was that they were Protestant.

The Nicholls had turned their pram into a T-shaped cart with a wooden box at the back for a seat. When Sean got too big for our pram I assumed my Da would make us a cart, too. We were all set to put the flag of the Eighth Cavalry on it, that one I'd made by painting crossed swords on an old drying cloth. And then Danny arrived and my Ma put a fresh set of blue-and-white rattles on it instead.

Eventually Danny got his legs under him too. I can picture him staggering across the breakfast room from my Ma to my Da, chubby arms flailing out for holds on legs and chairs. 'C'mon now,' my Da says. 'Two inches more. You can do it.' And then Danny makes that last triumphant dive, and gets the big hug and hears the 'Who's a quare wee man?'

About time, I thought. Now we could use the wheels of his pram.

My Da laughed. 'Ah doubt we'll be needin' them wheels for a wee while yet.'

But Danny didn't need them any more; he was walking.

'Aye,' my Ma said, 'but there's another wee Kerr on the way that might be glad o' them.'

So the pram sat gathering dust, waiting for Peter to

make his entrance into the world, while the Nicholls built up what looked to us like a Formula One garage. The bikes; the go-kart – a proper one from a shop in red and black; and that mini-motorbike of Ian's with the boxed-in engine and the fat white-wall tyres. They'd have races up and down the hill past our back gate, Rhonda bounding along behind them with her tail wagging. That was before they got her spayed, before she turned from golden Lab to golden slug.

Ian might have been gangly, almost a man, but he was a big kid on that bike. He couldn't ride it without sending gravel and dust flying from his tyres. When he saw me watching him that day, he braked so suddenly at my feet he nearly knocked me over.

'Want a lift?' he said, jerking his thumb at the pillion.

I did, but I was shy and nervous. I shook my head.

'Come on. Ah'm not gonna eat ye. Hop up on the back. Ah'll go slow.'

I climbed on.

'Put yer arms roun' me. If ye fall off this thing, yer Da'll kill me.'

It didn't feel right putting my arms round somebody I hardly knew – especially a Protestant somebody I hardly knew. But there was nothing else to hold on to, and I didn't want to fall off. I tried to join my hands round his stomach without touching him. I couldn't do it. He pressed them in.

'There. Ye're all right. Just don't let go.'

And away we went, back up to the door of the Nicholls' garage, then gently round in a big circle, picking up speed as we came down past Mrs McGowan's and Mrs Steel's and then our own gate, where Sean was standing, watching me riding a motorbike. It was a journey of all of fifty yards, but it was great.

It would have been a few days later when I plucked up the courage to ask Mervyn if I could have a go on the go-kart. He was no keener to share than I would have been.

'Naw,' he said, tightening his grip on the wheel, 'Ah've only just got on.'

'Go on,' Ian said. 'Give him a go. It's not yours anyway. It's Adrian's.'

Mervyn wasn't budging, so Ian hauled him off. 'Go on, ye wee shite. Let somebody else have a try.'

I didn't want to take it this way. It wasn't fair. Mervyn was trying hard not to cry.

'Go on,' Ian said, holding him back.

'Ah'll be quick,' I said to Mervyn. I wanted a ride, but I didn't want him upset. I stepped into the kart and pedalled like mad down the hill. At the bottom I jumped out, lifted the kart by its side and raced up again to hand it back. He snatched at it with a scowl.

'There. See,' Ian said. 'He wasn't gonna eat it.'

Mervyn glared at him.

Adrian was a lot freer with the go-kart, but then he's always been the softie of the Nicholl family. It was a weapon in all those battles he and Sean and Ivor and I went on to fight. Even Mervyn joined in sometimes, but Ian thought we were a bunch of stupid weans. He was already getting full in pubs; we were still happy with the tingle you got when you gulped your raspberryade too quickly and the bubbles went up your nose.

One day the Harbour Hill was the same place I'd gone to pick seapinks with Nurse Gilmour; the next day it was a battlefield, full of Injuns, or Germans, or Japs. It all depended which campaign had taken our fancy, which comic had the goriest pictures. Sometimes we were on horseback in a canyon, the rocks on its rim sheltering hundreds of war-painted braves. Sometimes we were driving tanks across a churning, squelching battlefield, yelling to each other about mines and quicksand. With a squint of our eyes, we could turn a harmless clump of marram grass into a strip of barbed wire.

We had to work the same trick on bits and pieces pinched from the yard or the kitchen. When somebody had a birthday and we were flush, we had proper toy guns to play with – until we broke them or stood on them (that was always happening with those plastic water pistols). More often we had to make our own. A bar from an old cot made a serviceable rifle, and the shaft of a floor brush a bazooka, and if you got them back before the evening your Ma would never even know they'd been out of the house.

A battle never lasted more than a day, anyway. We'd start hostilities after breakfast, have a ceasefire for dinner, and be ready to sign peace treaties by the time tea came around. You'd be lying there, flattened by a mortar, blood gushing from you, a leg and an arm blown off. Then Roisin or Judette would appear at the back gate and shout, 'Come on you boys, tea's ready,' and miraculously the blood would stop gushing, the arm and the leg would reattach themselves, and away you'd run down the steps.

The big questions were easy in those days: the British and the Americans were good, the Germans and the Japanese were bad. Most Red Indians were bad, too, except for Cochise, who'd grown old and wise in a way

Geronimo never would. So now and again we helped out Cochise and fought on his side as white men. After I read that story about Crete in a *Battle Summer Special*, and discovered that there'd been more than four countries involved in the Second World War, we even fought once or twice as Australians. The only thing we never did – and that guy Simon found it hard to believe – was to fight as Catholics and Protestants.

I don't remember us talking much about religion, but we didn't avoid the subject either. We all knew where we stood on football. Sean and I were Catholic, so *of course* we supported Celtic; Ivor and Adrian were Protestant, so *of course* they supported Rangers. But as we were all impressionable wee boys, and George Best was in his prime, all four of us wanted to play for Manchester United and Northern Ireland. And we did – occasionally turning out for club and country at the same time. We could play for whoever we liked in those days. Our grounds, our tournaments and our team selections were as limitless as our imaginations. Dr Monteith's garage door was the goal at Wembley. Adrian was John Greig of Rangers, passing to me, Jimmy Johnston of Celtic, to shoot past Gordon Banks of England.

And Johnston's through. There's only Ivor Paul – no, Gordon Banks – between him and a second goal. Johnston's tried a lob – oh, what a cheeky wee lob! Surely there's no way Banks can reach that. But he has! Banks has saved it!

Ivor was a great wee keeper in those days, and a brave one. It's a damn good job he doesn't hold grudges, for he's of a size now to get his own back. I was the big boy then, and I could easily shake off Sean and Adrian, but

Ivor was always so determined. The number of times I sent him sprawling in the gravel...Up he'd get, shins grazed, eyes misting, calling me all the names of the day. 'That's the last bloody time I'm playin' wi' you,' he'd say. And it would be – until the following morning.

Douglas didn't take it so well when I knocked *him* over. But then he didn't take anything well in those days. Why couldn't he have been more like his brother? We all got on well with Bertie, but playing with Douglas in those days was like playing with a bear with a sore head. There we were, the four of us, kicking the ball about on the hill, when Douglas appeared out of nowhere and grabbed it.

'Come on,' he said. 'A match. Me an' Bertie against the four o' ye. We'll run rings round ye.'

And so they did, and we let them. That way, we thought, they'd soon get fed up and leave us alone. After five minutes, they were leading about 5–0. That's when I forgot our strategy and forgot who it was I was chasing. Douglas was ten yards out, and thundering towards Ivor, when I caught him with a sliding tackle. I got the ball, not the man, but he fell awkwardly and hurt his leg. It can't have been that bad, for while I was still on the ground he came over and toed me in the thigh.

'You did that on purpose,' he said.

'Ah did not.'

'Ye did,' he bellowed. 'Ah know ye fuckin' did. Ye FENIAN BASTARD!'

That was the first time I'd heard the word Fenian. I knew a bastard was somebody you really hated, or something that got you in a bad temper – 'That bastardin' oul' door's off its hinges again,' I'd heard Uncle Jimmy shout. I was wondering what a Fenian might be when Douglas kicked me again, a real sleeper this time. He stood over me, hands on hips, daring me to hit back. I wasn't that bloody stupid. I knew he'd win. I looked away from him, trying to hold back the tears, until he walked off.

Sean came over and helped me up. Ivor grabbed the ball. 'Right, that's it,' he said. 'Ah'm goin' home.' He started running towards the bottom of the hill.

'Ah ye big weans ye. Can't take a beatin',' said Douglas, but he didn't bother to chase us.

When I got home my Ma was out in the yard pegging washing on the line.

'What's a Fenian, Mammy?'

She turned towards me, a frown on her face, and took a peg from her mouth.

'Why d'ye ask? Who did ye hear at that oul' talk?'

I told her.

'That's what some people call Catholics when they want tae insult them,' she said. 'Ah'm sure ye'll hear it more than once. But Ah don't want you doin' any name-callin', do ye hear? There's good and bad on both sides and Ah want ye tae remember that.'

I knew that already. Douglas was one of the bad ones, and I hated him. But I didn't hate him because he was a Protestant. I hated him because he was a big shite.

I wonder what he'd have thought if I'd told him all this when I bumped into him at Christmas in the Anchor. I didn't even recognize him, but he knew me all right and came over to pump my hand and ask how I was and what I was planning to do and whether he could buy me a drink. He's obviously forgotten all about that episode, so maybe it's time I did too.

Eleven

Twenty-five past three. I hope that's not my Ma I hear moving about upstairs. 'WhatinunderGod are ye doin' sittin' here at this time?' she'll say, and I couldn't begin to tell her. Here I am itching to escape to London and at the same time stringing out what's left of my waking hours in Portstewart. Sitting here in the company of ghosts.

I can picture Tom Canham in that corner, where the phone used to be before we put it in the hall. 'I'm dreadfully sorry,' he says. That was in the days when I thought dreadfully was an awfully English word, a word used by actors on the television and by Lord Snooty and the other toffs in the comics. Tom wasn't a toff, but he was English, and he was dreadfully sorry because he'd spilt his tea over my picture of Jimmy Johnston.

It was the picture I'd been saving for the front of my project. CELTIC – EUROPEAN CUP WINNERS, it said on the front, and then, in smaller letters, First British Team To Win The Trophy. (And then, of course, United won it the following year and instead of being the second British team to do it they were the first English team.) The wording wasn't on the cover itself; it was on the bit of brown paper that I'd had to stick over the top to hide the stupid flowers. I tried to tell my Ma you couldn't do a football project in a girl's scrapbook, but she wouldn't listen.

'Ah'm not spendin' money on another scrapbook when there's a good one here yer sister's never used.'

Jumpers, shirts, scrapbooks, comics – it was all the same. If they hadn't been worn out they got passed on. That polo neck of Roisin's with the purple and pink stripes – to think that I used to walk down the street in it! I must have looked like a right wee fairy. The black shirts weren't so bad, apart from the floppy collars. And when I was a wean I used to really enjoy the girls' comics: reading about the Five Marys of St Elmo's and cutting out Bunty and clothing her in riding or skiing gear: 'Bend Along Dotted Line. Stick Tab A to Tab AA.' I did anyway until that day Davy Murray leaned over my shoulder and asked what sort of a boy it was who sat at the table making dollies...

So I had to make a stand over the roses on the scrapbook.

'Sure ye can cover up the roses,' my Ma said. 'Stick pictures or brown paper over them.' She reached into a drawer. 'There's a bit o' paper here ye can use.' She held the scrapbook towards me and then jerked it back, clasping it to her chest. 'Quick. Make up yer mind. Do ye want it or not?'

I took it, with no grace at all. At least the flowers were only on the cover – the pages inside were the usual bluey grey. By the time I'd stuck on a label and the Celtic badge they were nearly all covered. And the picture of Jimmy Johnston was going to cover the rest.

Jimmy had his arms spread wide. 'Looks like he's tryin' to take off,' Bredge said, when she looked over my shoulder as I was cutting him out, but anybody who knew anything about football could see that he was doing it to keep his balance. His eyes were on the ball, down by his left foot, and from the way his right foot was raised you could tell he was going to shoot with every ounce of his power. The background had been full of bits of other players' legs and arms and advertising hoardings, and I'd cut it all away, leaving just a patch of grass for the ball to rest on.

I'd started with the kitchen scissors, but they were blunt from trimming bacon and kept getting stuck. So I pinched Roisin's nail scissors, and they were better, but it was still a fiddly job and it took ages. I had just finished, and was ready to glue the photograph in place, when Tom Canham came into the kitchen.

It's never occurred to me before but he looked a lot like Eric Morecambe: the same heavy black-framed glasses; the same thinning hair; the same habit of wiggling his nose like a rabbit. Though I bet Eric Morecambe's never darned his own socks. My Ma still tells that story of how Tom asked her for thread and she asked what he wanted it for, and even when she offered to do the job for him he insisted on doing it himself...

He'd been with us only a fortnight and already he was Tom to everybody. '*Mis*–ter Canham – who's that?' he'd tease my Ma when she introduced him to one of the neighbours. And he'd tell them he was a sales rep for an engineering firm and that he came from Skegness – 'It's a seaside resort like Portstewart, but not quite so wet.' I think he might have been the first man I ever saw with an umbrella. None of the local men ever bothered with them in those days; if it rained, they just turned up their collars and walked a bit faster. But he hated the rain. It was usually the first thing he mentioned on those two or three nights a week he came into the kitchen to phone his wife. The rigmarole he used to go through – getting the call connected by the operator, then having her call him back when he'd finished so he knew how much he owed my Ma.

He had a mug of tea with him. He set it down on the corner near where I was working and leaned over me. 'So this is the great football project. May I take a look?' I slid it across the table. I was glad he'd asked. He knew about football. When I'd shown the project to my Da he'd flicked through it and told me it was good, but he hadn't really looked at it. I was pissed off about that at the time; I took it personally. (Maybe I still do.) Tom went through it more slowly, running a finger down the tables I'd compiled, reading one or two of the profiles I'd copied straight from the back pages of the *Irish News*.

'Erratic temperament...' he read out. 'Yes, that just about sums up Johnston.' He closed the scrapbook and handed it back. 'Ten out of ten, I'd say, Michael.' He lifted the phone and began to dial. I got up to leave and give him peace.

'Sit down,' he said. 'There's nothing I don't want anybody to hear. Mrs Canham and I have long passed the stage of whispering sweet nothings. You stay where you are.'

He was looking up at the phone as his hand swept down, signalling that I shouldn't move. I saw the danger. I pulled the scrapbook away. But I was too late to save Jimmy Johnston. When the mug tipped, the tea sloshed right over his picture.

Tom banged down the phone and ran to the scullery for a dishcloth and a drying cloth. He dropped the open dishcloth over the slick of tea and began dabbing with the drying cloth at the cut-out of Jimmy. That's when he said he was dreadfully sorry.

I told him it was all right. It didn't matter. But it did matter. It was a black-and-white picture. The white of the hoops on the green-and-white shirt had been really white. Now they were all brown. That was bad enough. But in dabbing at the cut-out Tom had nearly separated one of Jimmy Johnston's arms from his body. It was a real mess. What the hell was I going to do? I couldn't put it on the cover now. And I had to hand the project in to Joe Fairley in the morning.

'Hold on,' Tom said. 'I've got an idea. Give me two ticks.'

He shot out of the door and upstairs to his bedroom, leaving me with the bits. There was no point in even trying to put them together.

I can see now he was trying to be considerate. I could see it even then. He didn't want to disturb me, which was why he'd told me not to move and why his hand had come down and hit the mug. But I couldn't help thinking that it wouldn't have happened at all if he hadn't come into the kitchen; if he hadn't been staying in the house; if we hadn't had to take in bloody boarders. Brendan Diamond and Eamonn O'Rourke didn't have people coming into their kitchen messing up their schoolwork, so why did it have to happen to me? And it would be a bloody Englishman, wouldn't it? (God, I was rough on the English in those days!)

'I'm sure I saw one,' Tom said. He'd reappeared at my elbow, and was flicking through the pages of a newspaper. 'Yes, here it is. Will this do?'

He pointed to a picture of Steve Chalmers, cheeks puffed out like Geoff Hurst's in the World Cup final. His right foot was up nearly level with his face; he must have just blasted a volley. There was no ball in it, but it wasn't a bad picture. And Chalmers *had* scored the winning goal in the final. I told Tom it was great, thanks, just as good as the Johnston picture.

'Right. Well, I'll leave you to it, then,' he said. 'I'll go into the breakfast room before I do any more damage.'

Cutting out Chalmers was easier, so it didn't take long. I stuck it in the middle, covering the last of the flowers, patted it down, and put the project to one side to give the glue time to dry.

Then I started to flick through the rest of the paper. It was the *News of the World*. That would have been the first time I'd seen anything at all racy – and it was a lot tamer then than it is now. I was used to the *Irish News*, with its ads for First Communion trousers and flights to Lourdes and for concerts by those bands that all seemed to have been named by somebody's granny: Robin and the College Boys, Brian Coll and the Buckaroos, Frankie McBride and the Polka Dots. This paper was nothing like that. It had pictures of women in short skirts and swimsuits and headlines full of SCANDAL and BRIBE. There was a story, too, about a VICAR'S NIGHT OF LUST. I knew vicars were Protestant. Lust was a sin, but what sort of sin I wasn't sure. I got no chance to find out. Just as I started to read the story my Ma came into the kitchen.

'Shouldn't you be at yer project?' she said.

I told her I was finished.

'What's that ye have there?' She grabbed the paper and turned to the front. '*News of the World*. Tsk, tsk, tsk. That oul' rag's fit for nothin' but the bin.'

Holding it at arm's length in one hand, as if she was scared it might drip badness on her, she swept a few scraps of paper off the table with her other hand and headed for the back door. I heard the lid come off the bin, but a few seconds passed before it clanged down again. I pictured my Ma hoking about, making a hole for the paper and pushing it well down under ash and eggshells. She was ensuring that the vicar's lust was well and truly buried.

Doing that project was great fun, almost as good as watching the match itself next door with Oliver. He might have been nearer Ian Nicholl's age than ours, but he was still a big kid. 'You boys and that Oliver Madden,' my Ma used to say, 'I'm not sure which o' ye's is the biggest wean' – meaning that she couldn't be surer.

As we pulled the armchairs in until they were nearly on top of the TV, Oliver said: 'Just think – the whole country's sittin' here watchin' this.'

Which was typical Oliver bollocks. In the whole of Victoria Terrace there was just us and Oliver and his Da, and if the Maddens hadn't recently moved in, Sean and I would have been on our own. The only Protestants watching Celtic would be ones who hoped to see them marmelized. But Oliver was right in a way: there was hardly anybody who didn't know the match was on. Even my Da knew about it – and not just because Celtic were Catholic. He told us that he and my Ma used to babysit for Jimmy McGrory when he was Celtic's manager and came to Portstewart for his holidays.

The things you think will give you an edge when you're a kid...and I thought I'd make the most of that one. I mentioned it in school at breaktime a few days before the final: 'My Mammy and Daddy used to babysit for the Celtic manager.'

'Jock Stein? But he lives in Glasgow,' said Stephen Doyle.

'No. Jimmy McGrory.'

'Who's he?'

'Celtic's old manager. He came tae Portstewart on his holidays and stayed in Central Avenue. Opposite Preston's.'

'Never heard o' him,' said Stephen. 'Put yer han' up if ye've heard o' Jimmy McGrory.'

I put up my hand, but it was the only one.

'An' who's heard o' Jock Stein?'

Every boy in the class raised his hand. Even Yvonne O'Rourke was waving. Stephen had a good laugh at that.

I knew Oliver wouldn't laugh, so I told him about the babysitting as we waited for the kick-off.

'Aye, McGrory wasn't bad,' he said. 'But it was Stein got them here tonight. Stein's gonna take them through.' He started to sing, 'We're gonna win the cup,' and he got up and did a dance round the room. If my Ma had been there she'd have said he wasn't wise.

We couldn't believe it when the Italians scored first. 'That's it,' Oliver said. 'Catenaccio now.'

'What's that?' Sean asked.

'That's what the Italians do when they score. Pull everybody back into their own half so Celtic can't see the goal, let alone shoot at it.'

And that's just what they did, but Celtic still won 2-1.

The *Irish News* was full of it the following morning. There was even a story on the front about post-match celebrations in Belfast. BONFIRES IN STREETS ALONG FALLS ROAD, it said, or something like that. That was the first time I'd heard of the Falls, and my Da thought it was a great joke when I asked him if the road led to waterfalls. 'Naw, there's no water there, son. Not as far as I know. That's where most of the Catholics live in Belfast.'

There were plenty of Catholics by then living in Portstewart, which was why we ran out of room in the school and primaries four and five were moved into the Tin Hut. I wonder if my Ma and Da went there while it was still being used as a church, before they built St Mary's down by the beach ... Was the Hut ever deconsecrated? Deconsecrated before it was desecrated? I knew something was up when I arrived that Friday morning and saw everybody else out sitting on the green.

'There's been a robbery or somethin',' said Stephen Doyle. 'They're not lettin' us in.'

'Or a fire,' said somebody else.

'Can't be,' Stephen said. 'There was no siren and there's no fire engine. That policeman yer Da knows, Michael – '

111

'Mr Haddock?'

'Aye. He's at the front door sendin' everybody over here. Ye could ask him.'

'Naw,' I said.

'Aye, go an' ask him,' said Eamonn O'Rourke. 'Or we'll never find out.'

'Go on,' Stephen said. 'Don't be a scaredy cat.'

John Haddock. Our one and only Catholic policeman.

He asked for my Ma and Da and I told him they were fine. He jerked his thumb over his shoulder. 'Ah don't think ye'll be doin' much work in there the day. Ye'll be goin' over to the main buildin' or, if ye're a very lucky boy, back home.'

'Why?' I asked him. 'What's wrong?'

'Aw, just a bit o' a mess some bad boys made durin' the night. Nothin' tae worry about. But nobody's goin' in now except for the teachers. If ye wait wi' the other boys on the green one of the teachers'll be over and tell ye what's happenin'.'

I sprinted back with the news, but Fergal Cassidy got in ahead of me.

'God, ye should see it inside,' he said. 'It's a real mess. Ah looked in the winda. There's stuff all over the place. Paper and books everywhere. Glue on the floor. Windas smashed. An' it looks like our projects are all torn up.'

'They aren't?' I said.

'They are,' said Fergal, who probably had least to lose. His was the thinnest of the lot, and he'd almost had to be tied to the desk to make him do it.

I thought of all that work, all those tables, that fiddly cutting-out of Jimmy Johnston and then Stevie Chalmers.

'*And* there's bad words cut into the desks.'

'What?'

'Somebody's done them with a knife or somethin'. S.H.I.T. an' stuff. At least that's what it looked like. Mr Storey made me get down before Ah could get a proper look.'

My Ma didn't believe me when I told her why I was home so early that day. At teatime my Da asked me what had happened and listened all the way through, shutting up the girls when they tried to interrupt.

'Were you there?' he said to Bredge at one point.

'No, but – '

'Then don't com*ment*.'

It drives me mad when he says that; when he ends an argument by telling you not to com*ment*, and then you want to argue with him about his pronunciation. But it didn't bother me at all that day, because it wasn't directed at me. Bredge was fuming but I felt ten feet tall.

When I'd finished, my Da immediately started talking about something else. The subject of the Tin Hut was closed. But I'm sure he and my Ma must have chewed it over for ages when they were on their own. They were still at it later on that night when I came down past their bedroom to go to the toilet.

'But why?' my Ma was saying. 'And smear mess all over the toilet walls? Why would they?'

'Ah don't know,' my Da said, 'but Ah'll tell ye wan thing. Ah'm damn sure it was nobody from our own side o' the house.'

'How can ye be so sure?'

'Well, it used tae be a chapel, didn't it?'

'All the more reason for leavin' it alone. Sure nobody in their right mind would do that...'

'D'ye think not? Ye'd be surprised what things there's boys in this town would do.'

We were back in the Tin Hut on Monday morning. There was a different blackboard at the front; the smell of bleach and fresh paint in the air. And there were two new desks – the same as all the others, but of a lighter and cleaner wood. Fergal had been wrong about the projects; they were still in the basket in the corner where Joe Fairley had put them when we handed them in. I flicked through them and found mine, Stevie Chalmers still there, still covering a riot of roses. They hadn't been marked yet.

The teachers were behaving as if it was just another day, but we knew it wasn't. For one thing, it wasn't every day the headmaster paid us a visit. Bob Storey came into the classroom three or four times and talked in a low voice to Joe Fairley. When he next appeared he stepped just a couple of feet into the room.

'Gerry Donovan,' he said. 'I want to talk to you in private.'

'Me, Sir?' Gerry said.

'Yes, you Sir. Now. This minute.'

Gerry got up and followed him.

Eamonn O'Rourke nudged me. 'Did ye see that?' he whispered behind his hand. 'His knees were knockin' like the clappers. What's goin' on?'

Gerry Donovan was a bit odd; you'd sometimes see him talking to himself in a corner of the playground and chewing his hanky. But he never caused any bother in class. We couldn't think what he'd done.

Then Stephen Doyle, who'd been out to the toilet, came back in. 'That policeman's out there,' he said. 'The one that was here on Friday. Him and Mr Storey are talkin' to Gerry. There's a police car outside. It looks like they're goin' tae take him away.'

And that was the last we saw of Gerry Donovan. I wonder what happened to the poor sod...I don't even know if he's still in the town. And we never did find out what it was that made him flip. When somebody asked about him, the teachers would say he'd gone to another school, a special school. They didn't explain why, but they had taught us to put two and two together, and so we did. My Da was right: we were surprised at the things a boy in our town would do. Especially a Catholic boy.

Twelve

Dick asked the other day what I'd miss most when I left home. Him and the other guys, I was about to say, but that would have made me sound like a fruit. So I muttered something instead about the family and nights out at Kelly's and made a joke about coming home within a week if the wheaten bread wasn't as good as my Ma's. Mick Rafferty said in that last English class that London's full of wee Indian groceries and Italian delicatessens and that even when you're on a student grant you can eat well without spending a fortune. But maybe things have changed since his day. I know Rita Madden found it tough. What was it she said when my Ma asked what it was like to be living away from home and paying your own bills? 'Well, Mrs Kerr, ye sure as hell make a smaller hole in a packet o' Daz.'

My Ma's already putting things aside for me. You'd

think I was starting a boarding house of my own instead of going to college. Towels. Pillowcases. Sachets of coffee and dried milk in catering-size quantities. 'Just in case ye don't have time to get to the shops in the first week, or ye find yerself round the corner from another Archie Herbison.'

Archie: now there's somebody I won't be pining for . . .

Rafferty's always on about the need to develop an independent mind, and we take him at his word and argue with him in class just to show him how independent we are. But we're not really. Take my attitude to Archie. How many times a day have I been in and out of his shop since I was a wean? And how well do I know him? Better than either my Ma or Da does because if they want something they send one of us. So why do I still picture him the way I first heard him muttered about in this kitchen? 'That oul' Archie Herbison – he doesn't like Catholics but he doesn't mind their money.'

Mind you, he didn't do himself any favours. Still doesn't. From the minute you step over the threshold until the minute you leave you're conscious of him and Mrs H. watching you in case you might lift something. You'd think they'd know by now that none of us would bloody dare. We might have gone to school with a few boys who'd steal the holes out of a flute, but we've always known we'd be slaughtered at home if we did the same. She sometimes passes the time of day, but he's as tight with his words as he is with his sweets.

'Hello, Mr Herbison. That's not a bad evenin'.'

'Aye.'

'Could Ah have half a pound o' Cheddar, please?'

117

The hint of a nod.

Archie bends down, opens the cabinet, grasps the block of cheese with fingers still inky from the *Belfast Telegraph*. He straightens up, breathing heavily. He places the cheese on the mat on the counter. He slices it, weighs it, wraps it in greaseproof paper, slides it across the counter. He takes the money and hands over the change.

'Thanks, Mr Herbison. Bye-bye.'

'Aye.'

My Ma used to get herself in a real tizz if we found ourselves a penny or two short when we came to pay. 'Bring it next time,' Archie'd growl, and she'd send us straight back to make up the difference. 'Ah wouldn't give him the satisfaction . . .'

In the early days, I did think he was worse with us and that it *was* because we're Catholics. But then I saw that he was no better with Adrian or Ivor; no readier to let them have one gobstopper more than they'd paid for. He's as sour with adults as he is with weans. You hear men in there trying to draw him out on the weather or the football and he just huffs at them. 'Miserable oul' thing,' they mutter on the way out. And that's probably the size of it. Archie Herbison isn't a Protestant grump; he's just a grump.

Peter and Danny might do all the running now, but I've still got a picture of that shop inside my head that I'm going to have for years. Cans and packets and bottles on the right as you go in – soup and syrup, rice and sugar, baking powder, HP sauce and Camp coffee and big blue tins of Cerebos salt with the picture showing that wee boy putting salt on a chicken's tail. The forest of nets that used to lean against the wall . . . and you'd reach in among them trying to find one that wasn't fluorescent yellow because you'd been told by somebody that yellow scared off the fish. And you'd try to move them gently and they'd all fall over and then he'd start growling at you.

The nets were only there in the summer; in the winter they'd have a pile of those peat briquettes. But all year round they kept some fishing tackle in that cabinet behind the door where I used to hum and haw over a Toby or an Abu Koster while Archie stood pointedly clearing his throat. And on the left of that's the glass cabinet with its banked shelves of sweets, the Fruit Salad and the Blackjacks at the front, the dearer ones at the back. And behind that are more shelves, with glass screwtop jars of the real tooth-wreckers: clove rock, pear drops, brandy balls, mint humbugs and Reilly's Chocolate Toffee Rolls. And straight ahead is the counter, where Archie appears as soon as he hears the ping of the bell, standing in his nylon jacket between the till and the bacon slicer, smiling for Ireland. 'Hello, son. How are ye? Ah thought Ah'd break the habit of a lifetime and bend over backwards tae be nice the day.' Some fucking hope.

The Scilleys have always been nice. I don't know how they work in that shop of theirs, or how their dog stays so sweet-tempered when it must get its paws stood on so often. It's like a train carriage in there: racks of newspapers and comics pressing in on your left, the counter tight on your right, the whole shop tunnelling on until it reaches that store cupboard at the end. And that's hardly bigger than a wardrobe. Then there are all those towers of cardboard boxes – crisps and books and toys – swaying as you brush past so you're sure they're going to crash down.

It's freezing in there in the winter, which is probably why she does so much knitting – it's to help her keep warm. And he sits huddled in the corner, hands driven into the sawn-off gloves. But there's still a cosiness about it. They always have a chat, they ask how your Ma and Da are, and they never rush you. The number of times I must have stood in there, torn between the *Victor* and the *Hotspur* because I didn't have enough for both . . . By the time I got round to paying for one I'd often read the best part of the other. They never minded.

Archie McBride was another one who put up with wee boys dithering at his counter. 'Thran oul' bugger,' my Ma used to say. 'If he had somethin' in the shop ye wanted but had taken it intae his head not tae sell it to ye, ye wouldn't have it. No matter how much ye offered.' He was supposed to be like that to everybody, Protestants as well as Catholics. But he was never that way with us. Maybe he was better with weans.

I used to love his shop. It was like walking into a giant version of my Da's toolkit – empty of ornament but full of things to look at. Braces and bits. Blowlamps. Copper pipes and ball valves and taps and sink plungers. Fillers and glues. Saws and planes and chisels and spanners. Bottles of meths and turps and primer and stripper and poison. We wouldn't have known what to do with the half of it, but it felt like something we'd grow into. It did then, anyway, when I still thought I was going to be a handyman like my Da.

Handy! That's a bloody laugh. The nearest I've ever got to that was making all those Airfix kits of Spitfires and Messerschmitts and Junkers 88s. They looked great when I just stuck to what was in the box. But then I started getting ambitious and buying *Airfix Magazine* for instructions on how to turn the 2E that had come in the box into the 2G that nobody was making as a kit yet. And it never looked like the one in the picture and I always ended up binning it. The money I spent on those dioramas and craft knives and plastic cement! And the time I wasted dabbing those teardrop brushes on to armies of soldiers!

Archie sold all that stuff. Probably still does. But it wasn't that that took us into his shop first of all. It was the fishing.

We'd stand there for ages goggling, while he stayed quiet behind the counter, unpacking yet more tools or sharpening one of the pencils that went backwards and forwards between his breast pocket and his ear. But he wasn't ignoring us; he was giving us time, allowing us to take it all in.

'What are ye after, son?' he'd say eventually. But he knew rightly. Nine times out of ten it was fishing line – the thick, hairy, dark green one he sold at a penny a yard. His rods and reels were lovely, but they were well out of our league. He drew the line off a bale and along the brass ruler set into the top of the counter, squinting through his glasses at us as if to say, 'You're checkin' this as well, aren't ye?' Then he'd take that fat curling blade and slice through the line with one cut. 'There ye are.'

'Thank you, Mr McBride.'

'Thank *you*, son.'

There was no guff, no, 'Be sure and catch a big one!' or 'Watch ye don't fall in!' He wasn't talkative, but he made us feel as though we were men in a man's shop. We were customers, not weans.

If we were in McBride's, then spring must have sprung. It was safe again to go down on the rocks, to dangle your feet from the harbour quay.

The North-West 200 had probably been and gone. 'Fastest motorcycle road race in the British Isles', as I used to write in those essays about Portstewart. For us the first sound of summer wasn't the swallow; it was that change in engine noise of a bike approaching Henry's Corner. *Neeee-yam. Neeee-yam.* We could expect a fat book of autographs, two pockets jangly with the commission from programmes and a full house back home.

But it was the sort of full house we didn't mind so much. They looked heavy, some of those bikers, but they never were. Their leather might have been rough but their manners were always good. And if you had to give up your bed, it was better to do it for them than for the old men in open-toed sandals and grey socks who came later. When I went up to scrub the washhand basins there'd be *Motorcycle News* to flick through instead of *People's Friend*. I'd stand at the wardrobe mirror, take a squint at that petrol-blue zipped cardigan my Ma had knitted, and in a flash it would be the black jacket of a motorcycle cop.

Sean went the whole hog: he actually bought a bike in the end. He got nicked on it, too, by Raymond Thompson, hours after he'd passed his test. I bet they had a good laugh about that in the barracks. 'Ye know what I did the day? Ah nicked Mick Kerr's son for speedin'. Have ye got a licence, son? says I. Ah have, says he. How long have ye had it? Since this mornin'...'

No danger of that happening to me. I couldn't stay on one of the things long enough to learn how to ride it.

But I still like the look of them, just as much as I did then, those Nortons and Kawasakis and Hondas out at the front, between the summer seat and the wall. Most of them were spectators' bikes, workaday things, but now and again we'd spot a racing fairing and we'd know we had a competitor under the roof. We'd swank a bit for Ivor and Adrian:

'Yer man Phillips is stayin' in our house. He won the Two Fifty at Dundrod last week an' everybody says he's gonna win the Five Hundred on Saturday. Look, he gave me this sticker.'

'What are ye gonna do wi' that? It's meant to go on a motorbike and you haven't even got a pushbike.'

'Ah know. Ah'm just gonna put it on the wall in mae bedroom.'

'Ye can't – there's visitors in yer bedroom.'

'Well...Ah will when they've gone.'

If they put us out of our beds, I suppose they put money in our pockets at the same time. God knows how many lemonade bottles we took to Herbisons' and Scilleys' over the years to get the deposit back. And as the summer went on and the house got busier there were more chances to make a few bob. When you carried bags from the house to the bus stop, it was always a good idea to wait for a minute and look hopeful; usually somebody would cave in. You might be invited to the beach to keep some wee boy company, and of course his parents would buy you an ice-cream, so you could pocket the money your Ma had given you to buy your own. And then there were messages.

I'll find out when I get to London, but I don't think the English talk about messages the way we do. In everything

I've read, boys are sent on errands – not *on* messages and *for* messages. 'Michael, would ye run a wee message for me, son?' 'Would ye get a few messages for me?'

Danny and Peter don't do nearly as much of it as we did. Messaging was a bigger business when we were in short trousers, but then the boarding houses were busier. The women were always running out of things. Maybe they were on their own like Mrs McGowan and couldn't leave the house or the kitchen ('Ah've just this minute put a scone in the oven'), or maybe they couldn't find their own weans ('They're never aroun' when ye want them, but ye see when there's buns on the table. . .').

'Be sure and check wi' yer Mummy first,' they used to say; but as we got older, supposedly wiser, they didn't bother. We were part of the local workforce, a fleet of couriers on shanks's pony that any landlady could whistle up: 'Right, son, quick as ye can. A poun' o' tomatoes. Mind he doesn't give ye any oul' bruised ones. An' you keep the change.'

Pickings were leaner in the winter. Mrs Minford was about the only one who needed regular help then. She was so thin and pinched, and the spots on her skin were the same colour as the damp patches on her wall. That first time my Ma sent me round to her I couldn't wait to get away because I was frightened I might get damp too. But she was a kind soul; she always gave you something for yourself. 'Now don't be spendin' it all on sweets, or ye'll end up with teeth like mine,' she'd say, and flash you a line of rotten fence posts.

You'd get so used to people giving you money you'd try it on with your Ma. 'Can Ah keep the change?'

'Get away outta that. What sort o' boy runs a message

for his Mammy an' asks for money?'

But sometimes we deserved to be paid – especially when she sent us to the Fashion Shop. There can't be a shop in the town that's less aptly named. All those mannequins in twinsets and tweedy skirts and sensible shoes peering out at the harbour through that yellow film. It's like the wrapper on a Quality Street toffee. I suppose it's there to save the clothes from the sun in the summer, but they leave it on all year, and it gets so dusty and crinkly that the whole shop looks faded.

It's smarter inside. If McBride's smelt of curing timber, the Fashion Shop was all lily-of-the-valley. I always felt the need to check I hadn't trailed in any mud with me. The carpet was so thick the assistant never heard anybody come in. I'd stand for ages, face burning, among the girdles and corsets and suspender belts before she looked up from her *Woman's Weekly*.

At least I didn't have to say anything; just hand over the note my Ma had given me, with the money inside it. 'Right,' she'd say, looking down her nose through the glasses, 'I'll just be a wee minute...'

But it was always a big minute, and I'd thank God for the fur coats that hid me from all the boys walking past outside, and wonder why on earth my Ma couldn't have waited until the girls came home and sent one of them.

The assistant would come back eventually, slipping something in a bag – tights or stockings or whatever – crease the top of the bag with a long finger and Sellotape it. She'd put the money in the till and give me change. I'd sprint for the door, already shoving the package up my jumper so that nobody could see the unmanly words written all over it.

Thank God the Fashion Shop's expensive, so my Ma only used it when she was really desperate for a last-minute present for somebody, usually around Christmas. We were busier then than Santa's elves, running here and there for boxes of toffees and chocolates, for Sellotape printed with holly, or for a last couple of sheets of wrapping paper. We were in and out of Scilleys' so often we could probably have got squatters' rights. And at least once a day we'd find ourselves in Herbisons'. We still do. Or at least Peter does.

Archie puts up his bit of tinsel at the start of December, but there's no change in his manner, no sign that any seasonal ghosts are disturbing his sleep. It's not till Christmas Eve, or maybe a day or two earlier, that he turns expansive. You go in on the usual run, pay and turn to go. 'Hold on a minute,' he says. Reaching behind him, he brings down a fruit loaf from the shelf and hands it over. 'Give that to yer mother, and wish her the compliments o' the season.'

Scrooge he might be, but he does give you a present at Christmas – even if you're a Catholic.

Thirteen

It's as cold as Christmas in here now. Maybe I should light the fire, save my Ma doing it when she gets up. No, I fancy a dander later; I don't want the house burning down while I'm out of it. *Student kills family and boarders in Portstewart blaze.* I'll do it when I get back, just the way she taught me.

If she wasn't such a good Catholic she'd make a great arsonist. Nobody can touch her when it comes to lighting a fire, though she's kept none of her secrets from the rest of us. We needed a bit of practice, of course, after she'd imparted the theory. I made a right balls of it the first time.

She'd already raked through the cinders, emptied the ash pan and brought in a bucket of coal from the yard. She was down on her hunkers, pulling newspaper and sticks from below the range. She straightened up, began shaking the folds out of the papers, then stopped. 'Wait a minute,' she said. 'Why am I doin' this when Ah've a big son here can do it for me? Come on – ye've watched me often enough. Paper, sticks, then coal.' I pulled a spread from the *Irish News*, folded it in two and shoved it flat into the coal-hole. When I went to add another spread she put her hand on my arm.

'Houl' yer horses,' she said. 'We're lightin' a fire here, not linin' a budgie's cage. Ye want some air roun' that paper. Here, watch...'

Yanking out the spread I'd put in, she unfolded it and shook it out to its full size. Taking one corner in both hands, she rolled the paper diagonally until she'd got something the length and width of a sword. Then she tied a loose knot in it, turning the sword into an untidy doughnut. 'There, that's more the kin' o' thing ye want.' She passed me a sheet of paper. I took it and tried to roll it the way she'd done, but it got bunched up. 'Ye might do better rollin' it on the floor,' she said. So I did, and it was better. I tied my knot and held it up, and she smiled and nodded to let me know that it was passed fit for the flames. When I had done three more doughnuts, she told me to put them in the coal-hole.

'Now yer – '

But I was already lifting the pile of sticks. I dropped them in and reached for the bucket of coal she had set down beside the range. Again she stopped me: 'Look at yer sticks.' I did. I couldn't see anything wrong with them. They were in there, ready to be burnt. 'They've all slid down the side,' she said, 'and where ye want them is under the coal so it catches once they start burnin'. Watch.' She took the sticks out again and put them back one by one, squashing them down on the paper in a lattice so they formed a bed for the coal. 'Now ye can put yer coal on.'

The shovel was resting on top of the bucket. I lifted it and drove it into the middle like a kid digging at a tub of ice-cream. At first I got nothing. Then the sharp end of the shovel shot up and pieces of coal skittered all over the floor. I looked at my Ma. She started to giggle, and immediately stopped. She picked up the pieces and dropped them in the coal-hole. Then she came round to my side and held the bucket at an angle in front of me. 'Now put yer shovel in,' she said. I did, and it slid sweetly down the side of the bucket and filled immediately. I heaved the load up over the range and into the coal-hole.

'That'll get it off tae a quare start. Now, as you've done all the hard work, Ah think it's only fair that ye enjoy the best bit. Here.' She handed me the box of matches.

I struck one, put it to the paper, then another. There was a hiss and a crackle. I heard sticks and coal shift, and then that wonderful *whoosh!*

I came back three or four times that day to check how the flames were doing. I brought more coal, and then, when it was good and red, damped it all down with the slack. The scones that came off the griddle later tasted even better than usual, because it was my fire that had got the range going.

Suzy Robertson nearly broke her back against the range. It was her own fault. That wee bar at the front's designed to take the weight of a few drying-cloths, not an arse the size of hers. There she was, holding forth as usual, setting the whole town to rights, when she leaned back on the bar. My Da tried to warn her: 'Mrs Robertson, you better be care – ' And then – ping! – it happened like a cartoon sequence in slow motion. The bar fell away, clanging on the tiles, Mrs Robertson's legs shot out from under her, the fag dropped from her mouth and she just missed cracking her skull on the oven door. You shouldn't laugh at the afflicted, but we had great trouble holding in the giggles then.

It certainly took the wind out of her sails, and there was no shortage of that. She'd only been in Mrs Phillips's old house for a week or two when she started telling all the other women in the street how they ought to be running their businesses; how they needed to modernize, to move with the times. And they all stood and took it; nobody challenged her. Maybe it was partly because she was English and they couldn't get the measure of her, didn't know how to handle her. And she was so big and blowzy and loud, a woman who smoked *and* wore trousers. She made all the rest of them look mousey.

Or she did anyway until that day she found the dead rat under the bed. 'Mrs Kerr, Mrs Kerr, what am I going to do?' she wailed. My Ma took the tongs from the hearth, grabbed a plastic bag and went in and got rid of it for her. She was never quite so full of herself after that, and the rest of them had something on her, too. 'Huh, comin' in here tellin' us how we ought to be doin' things,' my Ma said. 'Fit her better if she'd look after her own house.'

'What's the new people down the end like, Annie?' Aunt Mary-Lizzie asked, and my Ma gave that wee tilt of the chin and sent the eyebrows shooting heavenwards. 'A funny crowd. English, ye know. Dacent enough. Just a bit throughother.' The all-purpose phrase of disapproval, meaningful and mysterious at the same time. She'll have been in a pub where the ashtrays are brimming over, or a café where they leave lipstick on the cups, or a boarding house where the sideboard's not been dusted. They'll all be 'throughother'. She uses it about families, too. She'll have heard on the grapevine that the so-and-sos have a son who's done time, or an unmarried daughter who's up the spout, or a mother who blows all the kids' dinner money on cigarettes. Ask her what she thinks of them and she'll tell you in a low voice that they're all right as far as they go, but they're a bit throughother.

'How d'ye mean?' I sometimes ask. She takes a deep breath and moistens the lips as if there's a speech coming, as if she's about to trust me with a secret she's held for years. 'Well,' she starts . . . and stops, as if she's decided after all that I'm far too young and loose-tongued to know the gravity of it. She turns away, throwing over her shoulder, 'Och . . . just a bit throughother.' And I'm left to guess, to mull over the possibilities and magnify them. There are families in this town, in this street, that I've thought the worst of, when all my Ma was hinting at was that their kitchen floor could be a bit cleaner.

I think that's how it was with the Robertsons, but then you could hardly help having a few hairs on your carpets when you'd got two golden retrievers wandering about the house. My Ma reckoned they made the place smell, but Sean and I never noticed much of a stink when we were in there playing with Alan. I wonder what's become of him. He was a useful footballer when he was at Preston's, but then they weren't short of those at the time . . .

The Protestant ascendancy. I didn't have the fancy phrase

for it then, but I knew the truth of it. I was reminded of it every time we met Preston's down at the Warren. 7–l. 6–2. 5–0. We were tormented – especially me. It was Joe Fairley's idea that I play sweeper, not mine. I wanted to be up at their end scoring goals, not down at ours trying to keep them out. 'You look at great captains like Beckenbauer,' he said. 'The reason they read the game so well is that they play in a sweeper's role. They can see everything coming, and they've got time to do something about it.' Well, I didn't have much time – especially in the second half, when we had nearly every red shirt in their penalty area in the faint hope of scoring. So when Steven Forsyth and Graham Carson came racing down those wings, they often had only me and the goalie to beat.

They couldn't have looked more different – one tall and blond, the other short and dark – but they were identical in technique. No Georgie Best dribbling for them; it was all in the speed. They'd run at the defender, wrong-foot him, knock the ball inside him, and then sprint past on the outside to collect it before crossing. Sometimes I cut them off, but more often they got past, and then there was only Stephen Connolly between them and a goal. Stephen Connolly had a lovely pair of gloves, but he was no Gordon Banks.

It was great to play with the pair of them in those district trials, on the same side for a change, and see them give a hard time to somebody else. I'd walk round to Preston's and meet them and then the three of us would get the bus to Coleraine and walk up to the playing fields together. Until that day they weren't going and I had to go on my own and I got lost. And when I did finally turn up, nearly in tears after wandering for ages around

Coleraine, that smart-arse teacher in the Clark Kent glasses from St Malachy's took the piss out of me. 'You got lost, son? In our great big city of Coleraine? Well now you're here, hurry up and get changed. Unless your kit's got lost as well . . .'

Bastard. I *was* only ten years old. But then when Joe Fairley asked if I was sure where I was going I should have admitted that I wasn't, instead of pretending I was a man of the world. That's me all over. I'm sometimes so frightened of looking a fool that I end up behaving like one.

If I'd got there on time and not in a state I might have done myself justice and got in the team. I might have played at the Showgrounds with Steven and Graham and helped them score a few. But I didn't, so the strongest picture I have of the pair of them is still from those games at the Warren, when they're charging down the wings, about to slip another one past me.

The walk home was always longer after a game against Preston's, the action replays more regretful. Those garage doors in Old Coach Road and Central Avenue got a bit of a battering. *Bang!* 'That's how Fergal should have hit it.' *Bang!* 'Bottom corner – that's where I'd have put it.' Back at the house, toecaps grey from the gravel, I'd trudge in, drop my schoolbag on the floor, fold myself in the armchair and look for sympathy.

'What's botherin' you forby your money?' my Ma would ask.

'We got beat.'

'An' who were ye playin'?'

'Preston's.'

'Was it very bad?'

'Six nil.'

'Could have been worse. Now, take that long face off ye and come and have a hot scone.'

But after a thrashing from Preston's even a hot scone with butter and sugar sometimes got stuck in the throat. There was never any crowing after those matches, and never any dirtiness during them, but they still had an edge. We knew, without being told, that Joe Fairley wanted us to beat Preston's more than he wanted us to beat anybody else. We also knew why. A match against Preston's was more than a derby match, because Preston's weren't just our neighbours. They were our Protestant neighbours.

Amazing, now, to think of the things the teachers let happen. Our Man United strip was all right; that was strictly neutral. But that navy one of Preston's looked just like Glasgow Rangers'. So when they played St John's, in their green and white hoops, the symbolism was unmissable. It was a junior version of the Old Firm game, the sharpest needle match in football. It was unmissable to me, anyway, at nine years old. But it must have been missed by the teachers. Why else, with nearly two hundred league clubs to choose from, did they send out their boys, in Northern Ireland, in the strips of Celtic and Rangers?

Now I'm a bit older, I can appreciate the other subtleties. There was I, the doughty wee Catholic, having rings run round me by two boys called Forsyth and Carson. There can't be many names that sound more Scotch-Protestant than Forsyth. And there was hardly a man who did more to kill Home Rule for Ireland than Edward Carson.

Fourteen

Joe Fairley would have been delighted if I'd been able to see ironies of that sort while I was in his class. He was a great teacher. Great for me, anyway. But then he knew I was keen, I wanted to work. If you didn't want to work, if you pissed him about, then you'd feel the slap of that Dunlop gutty across your palms. Plimsoll: another English word; we've never called them anything but gutties. I wonder how he came to favour that and Bob Storey went for the brigadier's cane, with that splintered end that made you think he'd broken it over somebody's hands some time...

Joe would have made a great headmaster if he'd lived, if he'd not run his wee red Volkswagen into that badger in the dark. Beetle meets badger – no contest. He had that knack of making you believe you could do anything: you too could be an Alexander the Great. Alexander was my hero in those days; I knew all there was to know about his accomplishments – or at least as much as you could learn from the Ladybird book and the work card that went with it. The King of Macedonia, trained by Aristotle in every branch of human learning, just as we were being trained by Joe.

Well, nearly every branch. He never managed to turn any of us into a Gaelic footballer. But then like the rest of us he was more interested in the FA Cup than the All-Ireland Final. He always seemed to have a go at the Gaelic in the summer, like a gardener who only digs when it shines. Whenever he started running across the green, pumping the ball into the air with his wrist, kicking it from the ground into his hands with that funny scooping motion, you could tell his heart wasn't in it; it wasn't his game. He could talk about it knowledgeably enough, tell you how Armagh and Down were doing – assuming you knew they were teams as well as counties – but his eyes didn't light up the way they did when he was telling us how Bobby Charlton or Jimmy Greaves had ripped a defence to shreds the previous Saturday. Maybe it was Bob Storey who wanted us to play Gaelic, or maybe it was something all good Catholic schools were expected to do at the time, as much a part of the curriculum as First Communion and Confirmation.

You'd think Confirmation, being more recent, would be easier to remember, but it isn't. I still think of those Communion-preparation classes, and how I used to envy Rosanna Morelli. Because her Da owned an ice-cream shop she could be practising all the time with bits of wafers, but I could only do it in the classroom. I never did get it right. I came back from the altar on the big day with the Host stuck to the roof of my mouth, and I was still trying to scrape it off with my tongue when the priest got to the final prayers. Easy to laugh now, but I wouldn't have laughed then. Those were strict times.

> *Venite adoremus,*
> *Venite adoremus,*
> *Venite adore . . .*

. . . *moose-trap*, we used to sing. Then Kevin Devlin got caught at it and got a hell of a telling-off and nobody ever did it again.

After First Communion we all had egg and chips in Lever House. Then, of course, it was just the place where Paddy Hilliard lived; I didn't know it was named after Charles Lever. To think that his stuff was considered racy in its day . . . it's unreadable now. There was me being thorough as usual and asking Mrs Ryde (ha-ha) in the library to get me one of his novels, and it took a week to come through, and so even though I knew it was pointless I had to take it home because she'd gone to all that bother. I didn't get past the first page. But at least I was able to say in my project that Dr Lever had written *Roland Cashel* in Florence, Italy.

I suppose I've my Da to thank for introducing me to the library – him and his J. T. Edson and Louis L'Amour and all those men with murder in their hearts and gold on their brains and Colt 45s in their holsters. If he hadn't asked me to change his books that Saturday I was going to confession I'd never have gone in to the place. And after that I was never out of it. I knew it as well as the staff did. They were really good to me, letting me borrow all those reference books that weren't supposed to leave the building. But then as I was in there three or four times a week I was a pretty safe bet. They let me have those brochures on Portstewart in industrial quantities, too, so that when there was a picture on both sides of the page I didn't lose one by cutting out another. I learned a lot doing that project. That's when I discovered that Northern Ireland's one and only VC, Sir George Stuart White, was born in the town. Portstewart man defends Ladysmith: it's like one of those parochial stories about a fella who narrowly avoided boarding the *Titanic*. And then, of course, there was our real claim to fame: Jimmy Kennedy, sitting looking out over the bay, was inspired to write the lyrics to 'Red Sails In The Sunset'. I'm always telling people that – and I'm ashamed to say I've still never heard the song. From the title you'd guess it's the sort of thing my Ma would slow dance to, but somebody was telling me the other day that even the Beatles have recorded it.

I did the Celtic and Portstewart projects while I was in Joe Fairley's class, and another one on dinosaurs, but I did nothing like that with Bob Storey. So what the hell did I do? I remember him being strong on the penal laws, and the bravery of the priests in running hedge schools when they were liable to be hanged, drawn and quartered. I thought of the priests at Devotions on Sunday evening when my Ma and Sean and I were standing belting out 'Faith Of Our Fathers':

> *How sweet would be their children's fate*
> *If they like them could die for Thee.*
> *Faith of our fathers, living still*
> *We will be true to Thee till death.*

And the colour of death was purple, and when we came out into the dark and the spray and the spume, that was the colour my blue tie was turned by the light off the sea. I couldn't wait to get over to the other side of the road so it would change back again, and my Ma couldn't understand why I was in such a tearing hurry.

Bob Storey was keen on the radio – BBC for Schools or whatever it was. He'd sit down, jut out those fleshy lips, call for quiet and twiddle the dial on his Bush radio, and then there'd be five minutes of static and shushing before he found anything. There was all that fairy-tales-for-boys stuff about Cuchulain ('I swear by the gods my people swear by!') and all that singing along to 'Football Crazy'. I still know nearly every verse of that, and I can't get out of my head that other song we learned, the one about the character who'd set his sights 'on a proud career as Spain's first pop-star mouse'. So I suppose Bob Storey taught me something.

'Did you learn Irish at school?' that guy asked me at the interview. He looked disappointed when I said no, that they'd stopped teaching it at the schools I went to. Maybe I should have told him I was speaking Latin by the time I was ten. I didn't understand it, but I was speaking it. *Confiteor Deo omnipoténti* . . . I'd been hearing the words every Sunday since I was knee-high, but I hadn't spoken them before; it was only the priest and the altar boy who did it then. And I wouldn't have learnt it at all if I hadn't gone on for an altar boy too.

I was so jealous of the guys who'd got new surplices when mine was only a hand-me-down, but I hadn't noticed there was no lace on it until Brendan Diamond pointed it out, and then I was sure everybody would be looking at me all during the Mass, and wee boys would be nudging their mothers and saying, 'Mammy, why's that altar boy got no frilly bits on his white thing when all the other ones have?' When we arrived in the sacristy to get changed we'd try to walk as quietly as we could over those bare floorboards, but the housekeeper always came out to tell us to shush. 'Father McKeown wants to know is there an elephant or somethin' in the sacristy.'

He was a miserable oul' stick. 'Don't *ever* walk between me and the congregation when I'm speaking...' That day I got the tickle in my throat and kept trying to clear it, he laid into me once we were back in the sacristy. 'A sneeze, yes. I can understand a boy needing to sneeze and not being able to hold it in. But there's no reason on earth for rendering every word of the Mass as a cough.'

We were nervous enough without him making it worse. Those first few Masses when I had to hit the gong at the Consecration my hands were shaking so much I always caught it with the wrong bit of the drumstick, and then there'd be a muffled ding instead of a bong, and I'd wonder whether I should do it again or whether that would just confuse everybody. Lighting or snuffing the candles on the high altar was tricky, too. Every time now at Christmas or when there's a power cut, and candles are lit and then snuffed, I'm taken straight back to the altar. There I am, lighting that taper and shielding it from the draught with my hand as I go up the corridor, and then I go in behind the altar and press the taper on to the top of the pole. I wait a minute, to try to stop the shaking in my hands, then I go out on to the altar and climb the steps. As I reach up, and I feel the surplice stretch under my arm, I'm terrified that the taper is going to come out and fall on the altar cloth, and the whole thing is going to go up in flames, with the half of Portstewart looking on. All ready to tell Father McKeown it was my fault.

The priests who visited in the summer made up for him. When you saw them in the afternoon they'd be dozing on the summer seats outside Mrs Kelly's or Gussie Lagan's, stretching their sandalled feet on the pavement. Sometimes one of them would nod at you, but most of them didn't recognize you when you didn't have your surplice and soutane on. They didn't know you were the boy who'd been kneeling behind them at the side altar that morning. In the sacristy before Mass, they'd be whistling away, asking you about the football, and then when you came back in afterwards they'd sometimes press a ten-shilling note in your hand. 'Were they buying your body?' smart-arses will say when you tell them that now. Well, they never bought mine. Sometimes, when I read about all the boys who were fondled or kissed or buggered by priests, I think I must have been the only altar boy in Ireland who escaped.

The Christian Brothers were supposed to be the most vicious of the lot, but in *Portrait of The Artist* Joyce has them do nothing worse than beat Stephen with a pandy bat. I wonder if there was any of that sort of thing at Garron Tower, whether Brendan Diamond ever got a thumping...

It's strange to think that Dick was never as great a mate of mine at primary school as Brendan was. I liked him OK, but he was no good at football then, and that was what counted. He was all rubber limbs, one of those two or three boys you hoped you weren't going to get lumbered with when you were picking sides. But Brendan was one of the best players in the school. I suppose it was that more than anything that brought us together, and made me so keen to take his name at Confirmation: Michael James Gerard *Brendan* Kerr. And because he was going to Garron Tower after the eleven-plus, I decided that I was going to go too. Whatever happened, he said, he wouldn't be going anywhere near St Joseph's. Why not, I asked him that day. "*Cause it's the Dunces' Academy.*"

I had the move to Garron Tower all arranged – in my head, anyway. I'm sure I never mentioned it to my Ma or Da, and I doubt if they would have sent me somewhere as a boarder. If they thought about it at all they probably had somewhere nearer home in mind. It was different for Brendan: his brothers were there already, so he'd probably have seen round it when he went to visit them. I didn't even know at that time that it was St MacNissi's College, Garron Tower. It was just Gar'n Tow'r. I pictured it as something out of one of my comics – a real tower with crenellations, set on a precipice like Dunluce Castle, Gothic on a sward of green. I saw myself sitting in a draughty common room with Brendan in the evening, our pens scraping over pages, doing prep like those boys in the Jennings books from the library.

'Yes, they're all ready for it,' Bob Storey told my Ma. I'm not sure she would have believed that. She didn't think as highly of him as she did of Joe Fairley, and she was always comparing St Colum's' eleven-plus results with Preston's'. 'Ye have tae wonder why so many o' them pass and so few of our own do,' she said. She didn't mean that they did better because they were Protestants and got more opportunities; she was hinting that we did worse because we had Bob Storey.

But when he talked about me, she believed that all right: 'You need have no fears at all about Michael, Mrs Kerr. He'll sail through.'

Fifteen

It would have been round about the time I was doing the eleven-plus that Fergus and Yvonne arrived. Roisin was on her high horse about the university. 'It's a bloody disgrace,' she said. 'They should have opened it in Derry. And we know why they didn't – they don't want Catholics to have any education.'

My Ma, practical as ever, told her not to be so stupid. 'Sure there's nothin' tae stop Catholics goin' tae Coleraine. An' if the university wasn't there, we wouldn't have those two students up the stairs. Another wee bit o' money comin' in.'

I was always conscious of that with Yvonne: her being a paying customer. She was nice enough, but she never really became one of the family the way Elizabeth has. She might have the nose of a Disney princess, but she doesn't have the airs and graces. She grabs a chipped mug out of the cupboard and my Ma says, 'Och, Elizabeth, don't be puttin' that oul' thing on the table.' 'It'll do rightly, Mrs Kerr,' she says. 'Sure it's only for me.' You wouldn't have seen Yvonne doing that. She was always a bit distant, a bit of a city sophisticate. Unlike Fergus.

I wouldn't have believed they made Scotsmen as soft as him. I thought I'd had a sheltered life in Portstewart, but things must have been ten times worse in Lerwick. He shouldn't have been allowed out on his own, really. You couldn't resist winding him up. The first or second time he came in to the breakfast room to watch TV, he hovered a while by one chair after another, like a helicopter pilot who's not sure where it's safe to come down. Two steps forward, one step back. Down beside Bredge on the settee, then up again. Finally he lighted on my Da's chair. No sooner had he settled his bum in it than Bredge opened her mouth: 'Fergus, Ah'm sorry about this, but that's mae Daddy's chair, an' he hates anybody else sittin' in it.'

'Pardon?'

'Aye. He says he doesn't mind havin' visitors in the house as long as they're not in his chair.'

'I'm really sorry. I didn't mean – '

'Only jokin'.'

Bredge would have got a clip round the ear if my Ma had been there. She was as patient with Fergus as she always is with the slow and gormless: knocking on his door when he overslept; chasing him to the bus stop when he forgot his books; piling his plate, telling him he needed to fill out. She would have been filling him out that day my Da and Alfie teased him over the eggs.

I'd had my own breakfast and was sitting reading in the

breakfast room while Fergus ate with Alfie at the table. My Ma had served their fry and my Da was setting them down a pot of tea. As he backed away from the table he gave a tremendous start, as if he'd been stabbed in the back.

'God Almighty! Look, Alfie.'

He pointed at Fergus's plate. Alfie's eyes followed the finger. Fergus looked, too, wondering what he was supposed to be seeing there. A hair? A creepy-crawly on the bacon?

'What is it?' he said.

'Two eggs,' my Da said. '*Two eggs.* I never get two eggs. Alfie never gets two eggs. What is it you've been doin' that's got ye two eggs?'

Poor oul' Fergus. His face went redder than his hair. 'I . . . I . . . I dunno what you mean.'

'Naw, son,' Alfie said, laying it on thick now. 'There's somethin' goin' on. Nobody ever gets two eggs in this house except at Christmas. Isn't that right, Mick?'

'Aye. Ah doubt Ah'll have tae have words wi' the missus . . .'

He and Alfie looked straight at Fergus, like two cops squeezing out a confession. For a minute I thought Fergus was going to cry. Then my Da slapped him on the back. 'It's all right, son. We're only takin' a han' out o' ye. Eat yer breakfast.'

And he did eat it, but he looked as if it was choking him. The two eggs were wasted on poor, gullible Fergus.

But the poteen wasn't. He didn't get any of that. I suppose they thought that at eighteen he still wasn't man enough for it. But my Da and Tom Canham and Alfie had plenty. Alfie Lemon. Lemon Squeezy. He thinks we call

146

him that after those bottles of washing-up liquid; and we do, officially, but unofficially he's Lemon Squeezy because he used to be always squeezing the girls. Always after a few drinks, anyway. But he didn't mean any harm; he couldn't help it. If he's one of those telephone engineers who have to climb the poles, he must have found it far from easy after a night on the tear with my Da. It used to leave him wrecked, that spiky hair of his at breakfast sitting up like the teeth of a saw.

'Did ye not hear all that racket last night?' my Ma said on one of the mornings after. 'Them three boys singin' their heads off in the breakfast room?'

I'd heard all right. My Da and Tom and Alfie howling 'The Wild Rover'. Then my Ma supplying the percussion – banging the heel of her shoe on the bedroom lino. When that didn't work she went down to them.

'Yer father was sittin' there in the armchair with a fit o' the giggles. And do ye know what Alfie and Tom were tryin' tae do? The pair o' them were tryin' to stan' on their heads along the wall by the fireplace. Ye'd think men o' their age would have a bit o' sense, wouldn't ye? C'mon, I said, it's time you crowd o' boys was all in yer beds. For they were that drunk none of them was fit tae sit, let alone stan'.'

She had a laugh over it that time, but she hasn't laughed much lately. 'WhatinunderGod am I gonna do wi' yer Daddy?' she says.

Nothing much is the short answer. The girls tried, and look what happened: my Ma got an earful for encouraging them to gang up on him. And she'd told them not to, that it wouldn't do any good. He'd come back from the Anchor that day about three in the afternoon. He thought he was full of fun, but he was just full of drink.

'Would there be any dinner for a workin' man?'

'Huh. Some work you've been doin',' my Ma said. 'There's a chop in the oven, but Ah'm sure it's ruined by now.' He sat down, expecting to be waited on, and so he was. My Ma set the plate before him, and a knife and fork and the salt cellar.

'He's nobody tae blame but himsel',' Roisin said.

'What?' my Da said.

'If yer dinner's ruined,' Roisin said, 'it's yer own fault for sittin' half the day in the Anchor.'

'Ah was not. Ah had a wee drink,' he said.

'Huh, some wee drink,' Judette said. My Ma shot her a warning look, a leave-him-alone look, but Judette ignored it.

'Daddy,' she said, softer this time, 'ye can't go on like this. We all love ye, but we all hate tae see ye full, and that's usually the way ye are these days.'

My Da slammed down his knife and fork.

'She's right, Daddy,' Trish started to say.

'So ye're all bloody at mae now, are ye?'

'We're not,' Trish said. 'It's just that every penny Mummy earns in the house you're spendin' in the pub. An' then ye come home like a bear with a sore head.'

My Da got up. 'It's no bloody wonder Ah've a sore head when Ah have tae listen tae this,' he said.

'Mick,' my Ma started to say, 'sit down and finish – '

But he was already at the door. He opened it, slammed it behind him, and then we heard the front door slam, too.

I don't think I'd realized until then just how much my Da was drinking. I felt sorry for him and ashamed at the same time. Sorry that the girls were ganging up on him, for I knew that would make him feel guilty, and ashamed that he was spending the wee bit that my Ma earned in the house. I'd noticed that his chisels and planes, that he'd once kept so sharp and shiny, were going to rust. I'd thought it was because jobs were hard to come by, and that at fifty-odd he was getting too old to be standing on scaffolding or climbing ladders. But now I knew better. I knew it was the drink that was rusting them.

When we started studying *Sons and Lovers*, I pictured my Ma and my Da as Mr and Mrs Morel. How was it she used to view him? *She would not be content with the little he might be; she would have him the much that he ought to be.* My Ma's never been like that. She doesn't want to turn him into something he isn't. She knows he's not like her, that he can't sit in the house in the evenings, that he loves the company in the pub. She just wishes he'd drink a bit less while he's there.

So does everybody else. Derek found it tough last time he was home from Australia. He knows three pints is his limit, but my Da was always on at him to have another one, and bought it even when Derek said no. But what can you do? You don't want a row with your father-in-law. There's enough of those already between my Da and David. But then David got Anne pregnant before they were married, and David played in an Orange band on the Twelfth, and David loses the rag when he's pissed and says things he regrets. I don't think I've ever seen Derek pissed, and I can't imagine him ever being pissed enough to call my Ma an oul' Fenian bitch.

Mind you, my Ma and Da weren't much keener on Derek at the outset than they were on David. They wouldn't have known a lot more about him then than Sean and I did: that he was some boy going out with Judette, that he was mad about MG sports cars and that he was a Protestant.

They can't have been seeing each other that long when he went off to Australia. Judette told us all he was going for a year and when he came home they'd get back together. 'Do ye think so?' my Da said. 'I think that kiss ye got at the airport might have tae last ye a bit longer . . .'

The blue airmail letters came and went, and Judette got teased. 'C'mon. Stop pinin'. There's plenty more fish in the sea.' She got advice, too, sometimes in private, sometimes in the presence of wee boys with big ears. 'Anyway, if he did come back, an' anythin' came of it, ye know what sort of name-callin' the pair o' ye could expect . . .'

'Och, not round here, Mummy.'

'Ye think not?'

'People round here have more sense.'

'Aye. Some of them do.'

Judette knew that already. And she knew that there were people who didn't want Catholics in their kitchen any more than they wanted them in the family. All those certificates from the catering college weren't much damn use to her. Time after time she came back from interviews with the same long face.

'Well, love, how did it go?' my Ma asked.

'Ah haven't got it.'

'Ye mean they told ye there an' then?' my Da said.

'No, but – '

'Then don't be throwin' in the towel yet. At least wait till ye hear from them.'

'Ah don't need a bit o' paper tae tell me.'

'Why's that?' my Ma said.

'Why d'ye think? The usual reason. There were three girls there not nearly as well qualified as me an' Ah *know* one o' them's got it.'

My Ma shrugged. 'Well, maybe it wasn't meant tae be. It'd be a long journey for ye every day, anyway. Come an' sit down and have a cup o' tea.'

But Judy didn't want any tea. She was already heading up the stairs, holding back the tears.

And as soon as she'd gone, the story of Danny and the teaching job was trotted out again. 'There he is, wi' God knows how many letters after his name, and what do they do? They give the job to some boy who's not fit to tie Danny's laces. An' d'ye know why he got it? 'Cause his Da's in the same Orange Lodge as the headmaster.'

Every time I hear that story I feel sorry for Danny. But I didn't feel nearly as sorry for him then as I felt for Judette. Danny was a cousin with a mischievous sense of humour I saw maybe four or five times a year. Judette was my big sister – my favourite sister then, though I wouldn't have hurt any of the rest of them by saying so. When I was small and had nightmares, she'd come and soothe me, take me into her bed for a while and give me a cuddle until the demons had gone. When I got bigger and had rows with Bredge, Judette would come and patch things up and make us friends again. When she started at the catering college, and came home full of ideas and made fancy meals, she didn't get upset when I said they were too spicy; she cooked something extra, plain and simple, just for me. I thought it was a sad country where a girl like that couldn't find a job.

Sixteen

Not that I knew then just *how* sad it was. I'd catch a couple of sentences on the radio about Catholics being denied houses, and then twist the dial back to the charts; I'd see a headline in the paper about rioting in Derry, and scrunch it up in a ball to light the fire. When that kid Peter Dalzell came to spend the summer in the house in Hillside, I'm sure we must have asked him what it was like to live in Belfast. But that's not what I remember. What I remember is playing football with him, and hearing him say, 'This grass is really lush,' and thinking lush was a great word and using it every chance I got.

The only news that moved me then was in the football pages; the only job I could imagine myself doing was the one Bestie did for Man United and Northern Ireland. That was in the days when he hadn't got choosy about what he lent his name to. On he'd come in those ads, immediately after the butcher, hold up the fork, flash that big grin and say: 'What the man means is...Cookstown are the best family sausages.' So my Ma had to buy them for us.

But she wouldn't let us grow our hair like Georgie's. She was still trimming Peter's and Danny's herself, but she was sending Sean and me once a month to Johnny Stevenson. Johnny – slow of speech but quick with clippers. 'Do–do–do–d'ye want muh–muh–much off?' he always asked. But the clippers didn't stutter; they were already tearing through your hair like a mower through grass. Anyway, it didn't matter what we wanted; he knew what our Ma wanted, and it was her money he'd be taking from us when he was done.

'I don't know what's wrong wi' Johnny Stevenson,' my Ma said when Anne started making us appointments with Teresa Duffy. 'Och, Mummy, Johnny's awful old-fashioned.' And then we decided that Teresa was getting a bit old-fashioned and moved on to Guy and Girl. 'Coleraine? Sure what would be takin' ye tae Coleraine?' my Ma says now. 'I remember when I couldn't get ye to go the length of the town to get yer hair cut.' Aye. But then Johnny Stevenson didn't have anybody working for him with eyelashes as long as Kim Britcher's.

Why did Johnny never have even one comic that we hadn't already read? While you were waiting to be scalped there was nothing to do but fill him in on the health of your muh–muh–mother and fa–fa–father and look round the shop. Tongue-and-groove panelling painted with black gloss. Walls above that a dirty shade of cream. A round clock with Roman numerals like the one at school. A Clark Gable lookalike winking down from a

Brylcreem poster. And that mysterious ad for a Styptic pencil. I never saw anybody ask for a Styptic pencil and never saw Johnny sell one, so I thought it must be the 'Something for the weekend' in all those jokes. It was ages before I discovered it was for dabbing on your chin when you cut yourself shaving.

'Tell him nice an' neat, but he's not tae make scaldies of ye,' my Ma used to say, wagging her finger at us as we left the house. I don't know why she bothered. We passed on the message, but Johnny still sent us out pink and raw, like two fledglings stunned by a fall from the nest. Sean would get annoyed because I insisted on going the back way home to make sure we didn't bump into anybody we knew. It was even worse when Monday came round: there was nothing more shameful than going to school with a haircut your mother had ordered. Or so I thought. Until I failed the eleven-plus.

It would have to have been 1969, wouldn't it? So every time the TV and the papers are reminding us when the Troubles started, I'm reminded of when the letter arrived: the letter that said I wouldn't be going to Garron Tower; that I was all washed up at the age of ten and three-quarters. The worst thing was the feeling that I'd let everybody else down. The teachers all looked at me like punters who've put their shirts on the favourite and seen him fall at the first fence.

My Ma wasn't like that, of course. She kept telling me not to worry. It must have been nerves – that's what everybody said. She read me that story from the *Irish News*. 'Here, listen tae this: "Three former pupils of the Star of the Sea Secondary School, Ballycastle, who had failed their eleven–plus examination, have since qualified as teachers." D'ye hear that? So there's no need for that long face. It's not the end o' the world.'

But it felt like it at the time. The blazer was a constant reminder that I'd screwed up. If I'd passed, if I'd been the first boy in the family going to somewhere like Garron Tower, there'd have been no option but to buy me a new one. But because I'd failed and was going to St Joseph's I could make do with Bredge's old one, with that tell-tale pink piping instead of the new black bias binding round the lapel. 'Will he be needin' a blazer, too?' the man in McFeely's asked as he tugged at the pleats of my Terylene trousers and straightened the arms of my grey pullover.

'No, thank you, dear,' my Ma said. 'There's a blazer at home that'll do him rightly for now.'

'But it's a girl's blazer,' I told her. 'Everybody'll be laughin' at me.'

'They will not. Sure the only difference is that it buttons tae the left instead o' the right. Who's goin' tae notice that?'

She was right. Nobody did but me, so I put up with it. But the underpants were a different matter.

That first day at the swimming baths I was mortified. I'd put my trunks on under my trousers that morning at home, so I didn't notice before we went in the water. But I noticed all right when we came out afterwards, when we were trying to get dried and changed and the third-year boys were flicking wet towels at us, and we were envying them their big hairy cocks even as they were stinging our wee hairless ones. It was then I noticed that I was the only one – well, nearly the only one – who had no underpants. Why the hell didn't I have them?

Presumably, as Sean and I never missed them, my Ma never mentioned them. I suppose she thought she had enough washing already without making any more.

I did lay it on a bit thick, telling her I'd had the life teased out of me by all the other first-years and they nearly had me in tears. But it worked. I had my underpants the next week. And after I got them Sean had to have his, even though he was still only at primary school.

That's probably the only benefit he's seen of being the second-eldest boy. More often he's had to put up with the teachers droning on about how, if he works as hard as his big brother, he'll have no trouble with his exams. He'd have been spared all that if I'd transferred from St Joseph's, if I'd listened to my Ma and gone to Inst.

'Look, even yer own headmaster says ye're not really bein' tested, and a move might be a good idea. So think about it. We might have to pay a wee bit, but we think ye're worth it. Don't we, Daddy?'

'Aye, surely. An' when he's a professor we'll come lookin' for the big payback.'

But what about Father McKeown, I wondered. What would he think if I went to a Protestant school?

And that was the only time I heard my Ma speak less than reverently about any priest: 'You never mind about Father McKeown. It's not his education we're worryin' about here. I'll talk tae him. Now, will ye think about it?'

So I did, and I chickened out. I used the other guys as an excuse and said I didn't want to be separated from them, and I gave my Ma all that guff about how I was sure I'd do well enough at St Joseph's. But I *wasn't* sure, and I did want to go to Inst. I just thought I'd left it too late by then to make the switch. It would be tough enough being a Catholic boy at a Protestant grammar school; but I'd be a Catholic boy starting two years after everybody else.

I suppose I got a taste of how it might have been when they moved me on a year at St Joseph's. I got the same line then from J. J., sitting in his office with that black gown on as if he was the head of Greyfriars: 'You're not being tested, Michael. What would you think about moving up from 3J to 4J?' I obviously didn't think at all, because if I had I'd have seen what was coming and said no.

Chinner thought it was a great laugh. 'Come on,' he said, pulling three or four of the other guys in around me at breaktime. 'Heads together. Let's see if he really has got a bigger brain.'

'Why didn't they ask me?' Pauline McIntyre said. And they would have done if she'd got off her arse and worked. Figs could have done it, too, but I suppose he wasn't interested. As it was, he got more O-levels than the rest of us and he didn't stay on to do As. And Dick could have done it. He always had the most original ideas when it came to essays. When we were given that one on heroes, everybody else did a page and a half on George Best or the Blessed Oliver Plunkett and he did three on Che Guevara. I wouldn't have dared – even if I'd known enough about him to fill the pages.

It was murder for that first week or so. Dick was the only one who didn't take the piss. 'Lucky bastard,' was all he said. 'I've always wanted to sit next to Mary Lennon.' Then, just when I thought that everybody had got used to it and all the jokes were over, Mrs McKenna opened it all up again. It wasn't her fault – she'd been on holiday so she wasn't to know. But she could have been a bit more subtle. In she comes, sets down the handbag, takes out her glasses and puts them on. She's looking straight at me as if she can't quite believe her eyes. She looks so long that everybody in the class turns the same way, all of them gurning for Ireland. She takes her glasses off, gives them a shine and puts them back on. Yes, she decides, it's me all right. 'Michael Kerr. I haven't been away *that* long, have I? Last time I looked you were still in *Three* J . . .'

Which is where Charlie McKeever thought I should have stayed all along. 'Yes, he may be streets ahead in other subjects but he's not when it comes to maths. You know that yourself, don't you, Michael?' Yes, sir. So I didn't argue when he got them to move me back down. And nobody made a big deal of it. Not even Chinner. Not after that initial crack about the Incredible Shrinking Brain.

If I'd gone to Inst. and it hadn't worked out it could have been ten times worse. But what if I'd done all right? Would things have turned out any different? Would I have different friends; more Protestant friends? Maybe not. Look at Aidan: he made the switch and he still seems to think of us as his best mates, even though he sees us only at weekends. But then of all of us he's always been the staunchest Catholic, the one who blathers most about Protestant supremacy – which is why it was so surprising that he went to Inst. in the first place.

My CV would have looked better if I'd gone. Coleraine Academical Institution is likely to take you further at job interviews than *Saint* Joseph's, whatever your grades are like, and they would probably have been better. I'd have had more company in the sixth form, too. St Joseph's was laughable. Five of us start A-level English Literature and four finish the course. Four of us do Religious Studies. Two of us start French and I end up being taught on my own by Liam McKee.

That's certainly not something I would have had at Inst. – a teacher all to myself. Undivided attention. Which is why I nearly choked to death when *petit fonctionnaire* came up in that passage we were reading. I looked up at him, the neat wee man in his white shirt and dark suit and tie, and the giggles came on, and he gave me that quizzical look and I had to pretend I was having the mother and father of all coughing fits. For a minute I thought he was going to come round behind the desk and thump me on the back. I wonder if he ever twigged...

He was helpful and encouraging when I first mentioned journalism. I think he sees me as a foreign correspondent or a newsreader. He'd be horrified if he knew that what I really want to do is to go to the Hammersmith Odeon and the Roundhouse and review Linda Ronstadt and Dave Edmunds. He was the one who got me reading the *Guardian* and the *Times* – 'them big English papers', as my Da puts it. Now, when Maisie comes into the breakfast room with her papers in the morning and I'm already sitting there reading my own, she gets all huffy. 'Huh, Ah s'pose the *Irish News* isn't good enough for you any more...' And it isn't – not with its appeals for peace on the front and its death notices for IRA 'heroes' at the back.

'He's goin' on for a journalist,' my Da tells the relatives when they find the *Guardian* lying on the armchair.

'Journalism?' they say. 'Well, ye'll need all yer wits about ye, for it's a cut-throat business.' That got a dry laugh at the interview from the guy with the specs and the Professor Brainstorm hair. 'Cut-throat? Oh, I think you'll find, Michael, that we do a lot less throat-cutting here than they do in Northern Ireland.' But a lot more ball-scratching, judging by what he was doing with his hand under the table.

So, I've got into the college; I'm doing what I want to do. Why the hell am I still hung up on the eleven-plus? When I bumped into Brendan Diamond down the Prom a couple of weeks ago, the first phrase that jumped into my head was *Dunces' Academy*. Seven and a bit years on, and I've still got a chip on my shoulder the size of the Gun Rock.

It was the Gun Rock side of the harbour we did most of our fishing from that summer of '69. That was our last one, really, with Ivor and Adrian; the last summer we were a gang; the last summer before we all started making new friends. We'd started using slaters as bait, collecting them from behind Phillips's garage and cramming them into jam jars. My Ma nearly went mental that day she came into the scullery and saw them crawling all over each other trying to get out of the jar.

'But it's got a lid on it . . .'

'Ah don't care if it's got a combination lock on it. Get it out o' my scullery!'

What put us on to using slaters? Maybe I'd read about them in one of those fishing books I was always bringing home from the library. I loved the names of the tackle – ledger and paternoster – and how they sounded like parts of the Mass. I liked trying to knot the trace exactly as it was in the diagram in the book. But then that's me all over. Everything I do I want to do perfectly or there's just no point in it. Sean couldn't be bothered. 'Just tie the fuckin' thing on,' he'd say.

Which reminds me of that day I cursed at him and he ran home and told my Da. We would have been – what? – about twelve and ten then. My elbow was still sore from where I'd grazed it on the wall the day before, and when Sean tackled me I fell on it and it hurt like hell. 'Ye wee bastard,' I shouted at him, and then ran after him and kneed him in the leg. I'm sure I hurt him more than he'd hurt me, so I shouldn't have been surprised by what happened next.

'Ah'm gonna tell Daddy what you called me.'

'Go on then,' I told him. When he started running towards the back door I was sure that at any moment he'd turn and come back. When he disappeared behind the slope of the hill, I realized he wasn't going to.

'Sean!' I shouted after him. 'Sean!' I wanted to run and tell him I was sorry and plead with him to come back, but I knew that if I did I'd lose face with Ivor and Adrian. So I stayed where I was and pretended I had nothing to think about but kicking the ball against the wall of the shelter, when what I was really doing was waiting for the shout.

'Michael! Daddy says you've tae come in. Right now.' As he came back up the hill, Sean gave me that serves-you-right look, but he was careful to walk a big circle round me, well out of lunging range.

My Da was on his hunkers in the yard chopping sticks. He put down the hatchet and rose to meet me. 'Did you say what Sean says ye did?'

I knew there was no point in lying. 'Yes,' I told him, keeping my eyes on the ground and his pile of freshly chopped sticks.

'Well, Ah'm really disappointed in ye. I thought ye were a better man than that. Do ye know what that word means?'

I pretended I didn't.

'Ah thought not. It means a wee boy who's born before his parents are married. D'ye think that's a nice thing to say about yer brother?'

'No.'

'No what?'

'No, Daddy.'

'Do ye ever hear me usin' language like that?'

'No, Daddy.'

'No. Ye don't. Ah wouldn't even use it on a buildin' site. An' Ah don't want you usin' it anywhere. Now get back to the Harbour Hill and don't ever let me hear ye at the like o' that again.'

I remember that exchange because it was the first time he chastised me with his tongue rather than his hand. I stood there tensed, waiting for him to grab my arm, to twist me round so he could smack my arse, but he never did. I felt more grown-up being given a telling-off, but I felt smaller, too, because he'd told me I wasn't the man he'd thought I was.

And he's no longer the man I thought he was. Not the giant who carried me bouncing on his shoulders up to the top of the Easter Egg Hill. Not the giant who was clerk of works at St Colum's, and who oversaw the whole extension from that Portakabin in our playground. When it comes to their birthday cards I've never had any trouble at all writing 'To the Best Mum in the World', but lately I find I always hesitate before writing 'Best Dad'. I always think, Do I mean this?

If I'm really honest, I suppose I'm still pissed off with him over that Paul Simon concert. There I was, the dishes washed, the spuds peeled for the Sunday dinner, the floor mopped, just settling down in front of the TV, when he stuck his head round the door, licking his lips the way he always does when he's pissed. 'What are you doin' lyin' there like Lord Muck? D'ye not think yer mother might need a bit o' a han' in the kitchen?' And I'd only just finished giving her a hand. Unlike him; he was too busy holding up the bar at the Splash. But how was he to know I'd only just sat down? And if my Ma hadn't still been footering about when everything was already done she'd have been in the breakfast room with me and he'd never have gone in the kitchen and the whole bloody row wouldn't have happened. And he did apologize in the end, even if the concert was half over by then. 'Why are ye bein' so thran with yer Daddy?' my Ma says, and I tell her I'm not. But I am – still simmering nearly a week later.

At least he's not one of those drinkers who comes in and beats up the family. He just gets grumpy and annoying and you can't talk to him without getting his back up. I can't remember when I last talked to him about anything. But then he's forty-three years older than I am. We're hardly likely to be on the same wavelength.

Dick and his Da at least have the football and the racing in common, but we have nothing like that. My Da seems to have no interest in anything but drinking. He doesn't bother with the cowboy books any more and he's even given up on the music. I can't remember when I last saw him take the fiddle out of its case. If he had a hobby it might be the life of him. Maybe that's all he needs. Maybe he should take to fishing, like Archie McCauley.

Archie was always good to us when he saw us on the rocks; lending us a spinner if one of ours had got snagged in the weed; passing on a fish or two if he'd landed more than he could eat himself. Mind you, we usually had a fair catch of our own. At least they were always worth gutting and frying – not like those tiddlers the visitors used to bring in to my Ma.

'Mrs Kerr, could you fry this for mae tea, please?'

'Well, son, there's not a lot of it there, but Ah'll see what Ah can do.' And she'd take one of our fish, and cook that for the wee skitter, and he'd never be any the wiser.

We didn't mind – provided the wee skitter wasn't one of the Farquhars. They were greedy buggers. You'd take the supper trays up to the sitting room at nine o'clock, leaving enough sandwiches and buns and chocolate biscuits for everybody in the house, and you'd go back five minutes later to find only the Farquhars there and every biscuit and bun cleared. So you'd have to wait till they'd gone and then put up more for all the others. 'That granny o' theirs is the worst,' Roisin used to say, 'an if she's learnt no manners at her age she's hardly goin' tae start teachin' the rest.'

When Martin Farquhar started thrashing about and screaming in the Herring Pond and Sean and I helped Ivy Lacey pull him out, it was as much as his Ma could do to say thanks.

'Ye should have let the wee bugger drown,' Roisin said.

'God forgive ye,' my Ma said.

'The biscuit bill would be a bit lower if they had.'

'Aye, well, there is that . . .'

In that piece I read about Portstewart, the guy said that only Protestants swam in the Herring Pond, and that Catholics went to Port Na Happle. He should have talked to us before he wrote it. We'd have put him right.

Mind you, I didn't actually *swim* there until after the eleven-plus. Shoshua McKinney couldn't believe it when I told him. He leaned over the edge of the swimming baths until I could have rubbed my nose on his crew cut.

'Michael Kerr, what are you doing in the learners' class?'

'Learning, sir.'

'But you're from Portstewart.'

'Yes, sir.'

'And you can't swim?'

'No, sir.' And neither can my Ma and Da, and they've lived by the sea a lot longer than I have.

'So what on earth have you been doing with your summers?'

Well, apart from fishing and playing football, we did a lot of hanging around at the Herring Pond. At the interview, when they asked me about Portstewart and where it was, I cracked the usual joke about how far north we are, and how you could see Scotland on a clear day but that we don't get many of those. But we do. We had glorious days by the Herring Pond, with the sun beating down and the bathing boxes blinding white against a blue sky, like one of those adobe buildings in a cowboy film.

I believed for ages that Ivy Lacey owned the bathing

boxes, but even when I discovered she was just looking after them for the council it seemed a great way to make a living. She could lie there all afternoon in her costume, only stirring herself now and again when somebody wanted to rent one of those black rubber rings or hand over the price of a lemonade or a bag of dulse. Seaweed in sweetie bags, and people paid money for it! 'Full of iron,' Ivy would say, grinding a piece between her teeth as if she was an advertisement for health. She *was* brown – she was the only person in Portstewart with a permanent tan – but she was skin and bones. When she stood sideways all you could see were those big sunglasses. Peter had inherited the same build; there wasn't a pick on any of them except Karen.

Ivy looked so funny lying on her towel next to Bubbles: the one flat as a board, dry from endless sunning, the other all curves and ripples, water running down her like rivers to the sea after her latest dip. We never saw Bubbles anywhere but the Herring Pond and never knew her as anything but Bubbles – Bubbles for her sunniness, Bubbles for the way she was so completely at home in the water. She'd dive in, swim out and back, out and back underwater, and then surface. Never a gasp, never more than a sigh. I was sure she had gills.

She was always one of the stars of the Gala. 'Grand Gala Tonight at the Herring Pond' Ivy would print in her curly hand on scraps of paper, and she'd have Peter, Karen, Ivor, Adrian, Sean and me going round the town tying the scraps with bits of string to the lamp-posts. It did seem grand at the time, too, if only because there were far more people than usual there. Ivy would drum up all those game old biddies in their hats with the petals on, and all the would-be studs in their tight black trunks and Burt Reynolds' chest mats, and they'd get terribly competitive in the water polo and the diving competition. And the visitors all came to watch, sitting on the rocks and cheering and clapping as if it was as good as Hollywood. Mind you, they weren't exactly spoilt for entertainment; the only competition was the Sally Army singing to the waves at the other end of the town.

That's still about all we've got. And my Da wonders why we head off in pissing rain on a Saturday night to Portrush. 'That's a wil' night, boys,' he says, when Dick comes round. 'You're surely not headin' for Portrush in that?' Of course we bloody are. At least there's a bit of action there in Kelly's and the Arcadia. And what is there in Portstewart if you're too old for sandcastles and too young for crown-green bowls? Sod all. Not even a train station, because the 'quality' thought they'd keep out the riff-raff by building the thing a mile and a half from the town centre. So we've no choice but to hang around waiting for Ulsterbus when we want to eye up the talent.

There was a bit of that even at Ivy's Galas. Charlotte Swan was always one of the best divers – and she knew it, standing there on the tip of the board, flexing and dipping and bouncing up and down as if she expected a round of applause *before* she dived. Her boobs would have been bouncing up and down, too. But I hadn't got round to noticing boobs then.

None of us had. None of us was chasing girls, though one of them was chasing Peter. He would have been about five or six then, Caroline a bit younger. 'Is it true that you're doin' a wee line wi' my sister?' Ivor asked him, and he got all indignant. 'Ah am *not!*' But later on we saw the pair of them holding hands in the yard and we took the piss out of Peter, saying they looked like two wee girls from the back. And they did. Because he was the baby he didn't get his hair hacked by Johnny Stevenson, and it was nearly as long as Caroline's.

'Ah'm not a girl, Ah'm a boy,' Peter insisted.

'Yes, and I'm a girl and I love you,' said Caroline, trying to catch him again.

My Ma had been peeling spuds in the kitchen. She came out to tip the peelings into the bin. 'You be nice tae Caroline,' she said, giggling at the pair of them. 'Ye were happy enough tae talk tae her when she was sharin' her sweets wi' ye. She only wants tae play.'

'Ah'm goin' tae marry him,' Caroline said.

'Ye are not,' Peter said.

'Ye can't, anyway,' Danny chipped in.

'Why not?' Caroline asked.

'Because he's a Cath'lic and ye're a Prodesan.'

'Well, Cath'lics and Prodesans sometimes get married. Don't they, Mrs Kerr?'

'Aye, darlin',' my Ma said. 'They do surely. Sometimes.' But she wasn't giggling any more. She wasn't even looking at us. She disappeared into the scullery, throwing over her shoulder, 'Now, who's for a wee bun?'

When was the last time any of them had a bun in our kitchen? I haven't seen Adrian for ages, and I'm sure Sean hasn't, though he and Ivor are still great mates. Would we have kept in closer touch if we'd all been of one religion? Probably not. Look at me and Brendan Diamond: we were like brothers when we were at St Colum's and now we never see each other at all. That move from primary school to secondary brings big changes. Your horizons broaden as your legs lengthen. Your closest friends are no longer necessarily the ones who happen to live closest.

We were drifting apart by 1970, but I know we were all together on the Twelfth, because Paisley had been elected MP for North Antrim that year, and the Twelfth was the day his name came up in that weird exchange between my Ma and Mrs Nicholl. I'll never forget it because it was completely out of character. My Ma's normally so wary of giving offence, so careful to avoid saying anything that even hints at the political.

The four of us were leaning on the Nicholls' front wall watching the bands, Mrs Nicholl standing behind us. I don't know what brought my Ma out of the house – maybe she wanted one of us to run to the shop. She came up and said hello to Mrs Nicholl, and the pair of them agreed it was a lovely day. They stood alongside each other for a minute or two at the gate. I'm sure nobody but me heard what passed between them. 'Isn't it lovely that we can all come out and watch this together?' my Ma said. 'If it could only be like this everywhere in the country. . . and maybe it could if the likes of Mr Paisley would be more careful of what he said.'

Mrs Nicholl gave a wee cough. 'Mrs Kerr,' she said, 'do you think you're worthy tae be mentionin' that man's name?' and she turned her gaze back to the marchers.

My Ma hovered a moment, unsure what to say, whether to say anything. Then she retreated home.

What possessed her, I wonder. I wish I'd asked at the time, for she says now she doesn't remember a thing about it. Mrs Nicholl can't have dwelt on it, either, for she didn't stop Sean and me running in and out of her yard and she didn't ban Adrian from ours.

It wouldn't have happened to my Da. My Ma's never entirely at ease with the neighbours, but he is. He's expansive, sociable, confident enough to take the piss out of them in a singsong by demonstrating that he knows more verses of 'The Sash' than they do. Come to think of it, his renditions of 'The Sash' are a symbol of the way things stand in this town. We're in the minority, so as long as it's *their* songs my Da's singing in public, they're happy enough. But what would the reaction be, I wonder, if he stood up in the Sea Splash and belted out 'The Soldier's Song'...?

Seventeen

He'd never do it. He knows the unwritten rules, and no matter how many drinks he has he never forgets them. Nor does anybody else. So the nearest we've ever come to sectarian strife in Victoria Terrace was that exchange between my Ma and Mrs Nicholl.

I couldn't get that across to that American guy I met at Heathrow on the way back from the interview. Rob. The spitting image of Randy Meisner of the Eagles on the cover of 'Desperado'. He's probably conscious of that; probably wears the bandanna round the neck and the leather waistcoat and the cowboy boots because they add to the effect.

'Hey, I've heard so much about your Giant's Causeway. Would it be safe for me to visit there?'

A damn sight safer, from the sound of things, than staying in his own house in LA. I hope I don't feel the need for that many bolts and chains on my door when I'm in

London. How did we get on to religion? Oh, yes, he was talking about how he was going home for some family gathering and how he loved them all but Thanksgiving was the big one. And then we got on to Hallowe'en: my Ma's apple pie with the sixpences and thrupenny bits hidden inside in greaseproof paper; the nutcracker with the gnome's face that we used to break open the brazils and the walnuts; the rice pudding with raisins that we ate round the fire in the breakfast room. Why raisins, he wanted to know, as if I'd any idea. I'm sure my Ma doesn't know herself.

Then he got cute. 'Protestants have Bonfire Night and Catholics have Hallowe'en, right?'

'Right.'

'So you must be Catholic, right?'

I had to give him ten out of ten for that.

And away he went, hardly letting me get a word in edgeways. 'Hey, I really feel for you guys. It must be awful growing up as part of an oppressed minority... Still, all the shootings and bombings... Well, hey, you do at least know what it's like to have troops on your streets, to have your home occupied...'

And I'm thinking, 'Oh aye, Rob. I don't know about the troops, but I know everything there is to know about having your home occupied.'

If his plane hadn't been called I'd have filled him in, but I'm not sure he'd have been terribly interested. It's hardly Alistair Maclean stuff, is it? There were all those wee Catholic boys in Belfast and Derry growing up to hate policemen and soldiers, and then there was me, in Portstewart, and what was I doing? I was growing up to hate visitors.

I could have told him that I'd even thought of *joining* Her Majesty's Forces – for as long as it takes to fill in a coupon. That's why I was able to answer Rafferty's question on that very first read-through of *Portrait of the Artist*, when he was contrasting the babbling of the child in the first chapter with the language of the artist in the last. '"Old father, old artificer, stand me now and ever in good stead..." Anybody know what an artificer is?' He was dead impressed when I told him, wanted to know how I knew. 'Oh, I just remember reading it somewhere.' In a Royal Marines recruiting brochure, four years ago, to be precise.

But it wasn't a mechanic or a craftsman I wanted to be at the time; it was a radio operator. God knows why. Just one of my mad enthusiasms. Like that weather station I built and took readings with for a whole two days. Or the marionette I was going to make out of wood. Danny McAleese let me take home the tools from school and my Da bought me the timber and then I never finished the thing. I hope journalism lasts a bit longer. Sometimes I think I'm only going into it because Mrs McWilliams said I should do something that involves writing.

But the radio operating came from nowhere. Maybe it was all the films I'd seen where the hero's in front of a bank of dials and switches, tapping out the last Morse message as the ship goes down. And then when I saw the one in the advert he seemed to have a cabin a damn sight bigger than my corner of the back house. So I clipped the coupon, wrote 18 in the box next to age, and waited for the brochure. By the time it arrived I'd already decided that radio operators probably got sick at sea more often than they did in the adverts, so I flicked through it, looked up 'artificer' in the dictionary, and then binned it.

When I came home from school that day and my Ma started teasing me, I hadn't a clue at first what she was on about. 'You're a nice one – plannin' tae run away tae sea without even tellin' us . . .'

What?

'Some boy turns up at the door in a suit an' tie the day askin' if this is where Mr Michael Kerr lives. Says he's enquired about a career as a radio operator in the Marines. Mister Kerr? says I. Aye, says he. I says Ah doubt Mr Kerr's a bit old tae be joinin' the Marines. But he says on his form here, says he, that he's eighteen; might there be a Mister Kerr Junior in the house? Says I there is, but he's only fourteen years old, and ye'll not be press-gangin' him yet.'

I'd love to have seen it. But why did they send somebody here? Why didn't they just write or phone and make me an appointment? Was it because they'd checked me out and discovered I was Catholic? Maybe they couldn't believe their luck that one of us was thinking of joining them. I must have been out of my tiny.

That's possibly the only time my Ma's ever turned away anybody who arrived unannounced. 'Mrs Kerr, Ah know we shoulda booked,' they all used to say, 'and how busy ye must be, but if there's any chance at all . . .'

'Well, dear, Ah could probably squeeze the pair o' ye into the dining room, but Ah'd have to sleep ye out.'

So down they'd come to us for breakfast in the morning and up they'd go to Mrs Nicholl for bed at night, eating under a Catholic roof and sleeping under a Protestant one. If you were a stranger walking past here on a morning in July or August, and you saw how many people trooped out of our dining room, you'd have thought the house was a Tardis.

That Beach Boys' line about not being able to wait for June . . . I couldn't wait for September until they'd all gone and I could get back into my own bedroom. I got sick listening to everybody else in the class talking about where they were going and what they were doing. Most of them were only heading for the glen to see their granny, but at least they were going away. The only packing we've ever done – unless you count that weekend in Letterkenny – is to move out of our bedrooms and down to the back house. My Ma shouts up the stairs, 'Would you nip round to Scilleys', darlin', an' see if they have a few cardboard boxes?' and away we go. The nomads in that old geography textbook – we're a bit like them. The Moors of Mauritania or the Turkana of Kenya. We might not be looking for fresh pasture or water, but we're journeying in accordance with the demands of the season. We're moving from the top of the house to the bottom, from the front to the back. We're nomads in our own home.

I didn't mind it so much when I was a kid. No – I *did* mind it, but what I objected to then wasn't so much the loss of space and the lack of privacy as the fact that it was impossible to find anything. I could never remember which of those dozen cardboard boxes in the back house was the one I'd put my football boots in, which was the one that held the bound copies of *Look and Learn*, and which was the one I'd already searched through three times and turned up nothing. Sometimes things would get stuffed in a box in June and you wouldn't see them again until September. Sometimes you wouldn't see them again full stop.

That's what happened to the Billy McNeil autograph. When I lost it, I cursed the visitors for weeks. Mind you, if we hadn't had visitors in the house I wouldn't have picked it up in the first place.

It belonged to that kid Jamie from Airdrie, who went to see Celtic play nearly every weekend – and didn't he ram it down our throats! It was all right for the first day or so, this mixing with a boy who'd mixed with kings, but after that we got sick of him. 'No, you're doin' it wrong... Stevie Chalmers runs like this... No, Jimmy Johnston wouldn't do that. I *know* – I watch him every weekend.'

But he did have that autograph, and I persuaded him to swap it for a packet of Rolo because he was dying to buy sweets and his Ma said he'd spent all his holiday money. Then when he'd finished the Rolo he wanted it back and his Ma said he couldn't have it, that that would teach him not to be so greedy and that I had it fair and square. The number of times that scrap of paper got shown round the playground... It got as faded as the Turin Shroud, and was just as reverently guarded – until the day my Ma sent Bredge up to clear my stuff out of the bedroom.

'I didn't touch your oul' autograph,' she kept saying afterwards. 'Whatever was in the room's in these two cardboard boxes. So if it was there, it must be here.'

I turned those boxes inside out and upside down, emptied them and refilled them, shook every book and every magazine till the pages were coming loose.

Bredge had forgotten the whole thing hours later, but it was ages before I forgave her. All those fights I used to have with her, all that slapping and pinching. It wasn't just about whose turn it was to mop the kitchen floor; I was still sore about losing the celebrity scrawl of Billy McNeil, still furious that it was impossible to keep something safe in our own house.

If you can call it our own house when even the bloody name's been chosen by the visitors... My Ma should have changed it when we moved in. If she'd done that the plaque wouldn't have been propped there in the fanlight for that Scottish woman to see. 'Inverness! We just couldn't believe it, dear. We're from Victoria Terrace in Inverness, so when we saw an Inverness, Victoria Terrace, we just had to stop, didn't we, Hamish? Oh, no, you mustn't change it. It'll bring you luck.' And my Ma listened to her. She should have told her to piss off like my Da told that gypsy woman with the heather.

My Ma would tell me I'm being silly, but there's a symbolism in all this. Here we are, Catholics in a house with a Scottish-Protestant name. And every summer we have only a tiny bit of it to ourselves – the kitchen and scullery and the back house and maybe, if we're not too busy, the breakfast room. That's our side of the house. Our side of our own house. It's a sort of occupied Ireland with a difference.

Trish would enjoy that; she was always quick to see that kind of thing. I missed her when she went to Belfast. I envied her, too, because I was thirteen and desperate to get some space of my own and she'd managed to do it. The nuns at the convent were really sniffy. 'A *business* college, Patricia? A *secretarial* course?' It made no difference to them that it was bilingual. And now she's assistant to the Health Minister in Victoria. That'll show the oul' bitches.

When she was still doing A-levels, I loved hearing her practising her Spanish, rolling the r's, laughing as she lisped the th sound. She'd have made a good teacher, too. 'If the c's followed by an e or an i you pronounce it like the th in thin...Here, you take the book an' try it.' So I did, and when I'd got over thinking that a lisp made me sound like a fruit, I began to enjoy it. *Cinco cervezas, por favor. Muchas gracias.* Very handy that'll be if I ever get to Madrid.

Funny now to think she's in Australia, when she only went to Belfast in the first place because she thought Liverpool and Aberystwyth universities were too far away. When she came back at the weekends, she always seemed so nervy. The evening there was that big roll of thunder she jumped as if she'd been shot. Her body might have been home, but her mind was still in Belfast, turning every bang into a bomb.

But she hadn't lost her sense of humour. She was great value on the soldiers and their searches, on the young squaddie who stopped her when she was going into Marks and Spencer's for knickers. 'Excuse me, miss, I'm sorry but I need to look in your bag.' And she felt sorry for him, because she had a stinking cold and had shoved all these damp tissues in the bag and had meant to stick them in a bin but all the bins had been taken away because they were a security risk. And the soldier's hoking about, and getting God knows what on his hands, and he pulls out her lipstick and asks her to open it. I can hear the indignation in her voice now: 'Can ye believe it? He wanted tae see *inside* mae *lipstick*...'

My Ma and Da sat there shaking their heads and clucking at the madness of Belfast. Then they wanted reassurance that she wasn't going out at night – as if the place was any more dangerous then than it was during the day.

Chance would be a fine thing, she told them; she'd far too much studying to do when she got back to her digs in the evenings. But she told us different. She told Bredge and me about that pub she used to go to with her landlady's daughters, always on the same night, and how one night none of them was able to go. And that was the night they blew the place up.

The more I think about it the more I think I was right to plump for London. At least I have a choice – unlike those families the Red Cross brought to stay with us. Trish was bad enough, but they were ten times jumpier. They'd had to live with it for a lot longer. The mothers were all fingernail-biters and chain-smokers. And where were the fathers? I suppose some of them at least must have been banged up.

They hardly said a word for the first twenty-four hours; just sat there muttering among themselves. Then it was as if they'd decided that it was all right, that they could burst all those buttons that had been holding in their lives in Ballymurphy or the Creggan or wherever they were from.

'God, Mrs Kerr, it's so nice of ye tae have us.'

'It is. Ye're a saint, so ye are.'

'My wee boys had never seen the sea till we came here. We'd heard about the Port, all right, but we'd no idea how nice it was goin' tae be.'

'An' the people are so nice, too, an' it's all so normal. Ye see that car out there. Well, if ye left a car parked like that round our way the Brits'd blow it up so they would.'

But that wee boy Malachy never settled. He thought it was every bit as dangerous in Portstewart as it was in Belfast. I'll never forget that night my Ma and I went up to check on him. I was watching the end of *Cannon*, and he'd just trapped the murderer when she asked me to go. And when I said I'd do it in a minute she went herself. She was at the door of the back return by the time I caught her, doing that funny knock of hers, rubbing her ring on the frosted glass. 'Malachy,' she said, 'are ye dacent, son?' and she winked at me. There was no answer. She opened the door.

And there was no Malachy. Not in the single bed on the right where he was supposed to be. Not in the double. And not in the three-quarter. They were all as neat as the girls had left them in the morning.

My Ma thought he might have gone to the toilet, but the door had been open when I passed so I'd have noticed.

'Then where on earth is he? Here he is, not two days in Portstewart, his mother in the Anchor, me supposed to be lookin' after him, and he's disappeared. Well, he can't have gone far. His shoes are still here.'

She bent down, started to lift the shoes – and let them fall again.

'And here he is himsel'...'

She pulled up the hem of the quilt and flicked it back. We both bent down and looked under the bed.

He was curled up on the floor like a foetus, fast asleep. He smelt a bit. I think he'd wet his pyjamas.

My Ma got down on her knees and rolled him out on to her lap. He looked about seven. He was sweating. She took the hankie from her housecoat pocket and wiped his brow. He woke up then, and writhed about like some cornered wee animal. I was sure he'd sprint from the room.

'It's all right, son,' she told him. 'It's all right. Ye remember me, don't ye? Mrs Kerr. Ye're havin' a wee holiday in my house. Ye remember me and yer mother chattin' this evenin' an' I said I'd keep an eye on ye while she slipped out for a break? Ye remember that, don't ye?'

That settled him. He stopped the twitching. 'Aye. Ah remember. Will mae Mammy be long?'

'No, not much longer now, son. But let's get ye changed into dry clothes and back into bed. What were ye doin' under it anyway? Wouldn't ye be more comfortable in it?'

He looked at me, then at my Ma. 'I allus sleep under it, missus,' he said, 'just in case there's shootin'.'

I suppose that's when it came home to me (oh yes, *home* to me) just what's going on in other parts of the country, and how lucky I am to be living here. Our house might get a bit crowded in the summer, and you might sometimes lose your bed, but at least when you do have one you can sleep soundly in it. Not like that wee bugger, with the snotters tripping him, lying under the bloody thing because he was shit-scared to get on top of it. What the hell must it be like where he's gone back to, with the bangs and the shots and the rumble of the armoured cars in the dark and the squaddies kicking in the doors and lifting his Daddy? If I lived there I'd probably be as screwed up as he is. But I don't. As my Ma tried to tell him, we live in a different country.

'Come on, son. There's no need for hidin' under beds

here. There'll be no shootin' the night. We don't have any o' that kind o' nonsense in Portstewart.'

Nonsense: that's what it is to her, all of it, whether you're talking about marching or shooting. It's all nonsense. She knows Catholics don't get a fair deal, and she'd like to do something about it, but she thinks the answer lies in prayer rather than politics. So she says the Rosary, and goes to Mass and Devotions, and gets on with her work and her neighbours and her life.

That's one reason she wasn't overly keen on Tony. Tony made Republican noises, and my Ma was frightened he'd have Roisin making them too. He wasn't with us that long, and when he wasn't managing the pub he kept himself to himself, so none of the rest of us really got to know him. The fact that he liked to speak Irish added to my Ma's suspicions (even though she's the one who's always saying, 'Our own language, and not one of us can speak it – it's a bloomin' disgrace!'). He was learning German as well: 'A good strong guttural tongue,' he told me that day, as I flicked through his BBC course book. Maybe he just fancied himself as a linguist.

He was fond of lobsters, too. My Ma cooked them for him at least a couple of times. I can see her now steeling herself to handle them. 'Oh, I hate the look o' these boys, with them feelers wavin' about all over the place.' She hated even more dropping them into the boiling water. Sean and Danny and I didn't make it any easier by telling her we could hear the squealing from the saucepan, and didn't she know that this was the way the Romans used to treat the Christians. But we all wanted to be there when the lid came off to see the transformation. In they went, cold and greeny-black; out they came, hot and pink.

Unlike Roisin when she got back from that rally he took her to. Blue with the cold, and minus a new Aran jumper. Somebody on the platform had complained of feeling the chill, so Roisin handed over the jumper, and never got it back. She wasn't bothered. Maybe she thought it was a sacrifice worth making, evidence of political faith. My Ma thought it was daft.

Eighteen

I wonder if I'd be any different if I'd grown up in another
house – somewhere like the Ryans', maybe, with their
Da on this committee and that one so that they're talking
politics all the time. I'm sure they must be, anyway,
judging from the things they used to say even when they
were at primary school. They were hardly fifteen before
they had beards and trenchcoats and were walking about
looking like anarchists out of *The Secret Agent*.

It's never been like that here. The only one who ever
talks politics is Uncle Paddy, and that's only because he
has some connection with the SDLP, and by the time he
starts on it nobody's listening because he's arrived so late
we're all ready for bed anyway. My Ma and Da didn't
have much of an education, and maybe if they had they
would have been different. But I don't know. They still
wouldn't have been militants; they wouldn't have joined

the IRA. They don't believe anything is worth killing for. And I'm sure that's why I feel the same way. I might be wishy-washy, I might change my mind every five minutes about everything else, but I know where I stand on that.

I do wish sometimes I could find out what they really think. It's not just that he can't be bothered and she's too busy making a living. It's almost as if they're scared to talk about it. That's the way my Ma is, anyway. It's almost as if she sees a direct line: you start getting interested in politics, you get involved and then you get killed. So for God's sake don't discuss it with the weans – even when they're eighteen years old. I remember having that chat with her about the Alliance Party as she stood here one afternoon with her hands in the flour for yet another scone. Well, if you can call it a chat. I'd only just heard of the Alliance and I thought it was great that their first priority was to attract support from both sides. I put that to her and she nodded.

'Would *you* think of votin' for them?'

She looked up, pushed the hair off her forehead with the back of a floury hand. 'Aye, maybe, son,' she said, and went back to the scone.

But I'm sure she's never voted Alliance. I don't know what they used to do, but I'm sure that when she and my Da go into the polling station now they put their X next to SDLP. That's what you do if you're a peace-loving Catholic who hopes for a united Ireland but doesn't expect to see one; it's no more to be questioned than attendance at Mass. But you don't talk about it, you don't discuss it with the weans. Politics is like sex: something adults do in the dark.

In the dark, or not at all. And certainly not on our TV.

At least we can go up to Anne and David's now if there's something we want to see and we know my Ma's bound to turn it off halfway through. Parkinson will be asking some actress if she minds nude scenes, Dave Allen will be telling a good one about nuns, and then – blip – off it goes. And her timing! She must have sensors. A censor with sensors. *Play for Today*'s on, some woman is about to unfasten her bra, and my Ma comes barging in to the breakfast room, just in the nick of time to save her sons from sin. 'Tsk. Tsk. Tsk. What's this oul' rubbage? It's time this thing was off anyway.'

But she couldn't turn Brenda off. It's a bit harder to keep sex out of the house when it's being brought in by the boarders. Harder still when it *is* the boarders. For that's what Brenda was – one of those raunchy *Play for Today* women come to life, stepping off the screen into the kitchen.

I wonder if she had any idea of the effect she had on me? Probably not. I was just the wee boy who'd suddenly taken to polishing his shoes and combing his hair and who could be easily made to blush. She'd have known she was teasing, but not that she was a tease.

'I think he has a girlfriend.'

'Ah have not.'

'Aw, come on now, Michael. I know ye've a notion of that wee blonde girl in Rosborough's – the one that's always on the till.'

'Ah have not.'

'Ye have so. Oh, look at the colour he's gone, Mrs Kerr.'

Heat on my face. I shove the brush and polish back in their tin, slam the cupboard door and get out of the kitchen as quick as I can, Brenda cackling away behind me.

It *was* a cackle; a wild, unbridled laugh that went on for longer than any joke deserved. When the rest of us had giggled our last, she'd still have her head thrown back, throat bared, chest heaving. She wasn't at all self-conscious. It was us who got embarrassed, looking at each other and the walls and the ceiling – anywhere but directly at her – until she'd subsided. We all remarked on the laugh, but nobody read much into it until the day that amateur psychiatrist took my Ma aside after dinner.

'Mrs Kerr, I hope you don't think I'm being nosey, but that girl that sits on her own in the dining room, the one with the jet-black hair...'

'Brenda, you mean, dear?'

'Is that what they call her? Is she all right?'

'How d'you mean, dear?'

'That laugh of hers – the way she goes on and on. I'm sure she's bad with her nerves. I had a cousin was just the same...'

All my Ma knew was what Brenda's parents had told her: that she'd been through a rough time, she and her husband had separated and she needed a rest cure. Now my Ma began to wonder whether there was something else she should have been told; whether Brenda might need watching.

I thought she needed watching, all right. I couldn't take my eyes off her. I thought about Carol in Rosborough's during the day, but it was Brenda I went to bed with in my dreams at night. I wonder if it's the same for Protestant boys; whether they have a first love and a first lust... Or is it just us? Is it Catholicism that makes you separate love from sex, makes you dream of kissing a good girl and riding a bad one? But I'm sure we all dream of riding an older one. 'Summer The First Time': cheesy song, great fantasy.

She'd be what? Twice my age? Late thirties, early forties. And all woman. Husky-voiced, voluptuous, and not afraid to show it off. The tops with the low necks. The short skirts that slid up her arse when she sat down. The black stockings on those legs that she twisted and untwisted, one round the other, like two coiling snakes. Serpents in the Catholic kitchen.

I must have been sitting here with my tongue hanging out half the time. I'm amazed nobody noticed. There we were that day, cups clinking on the best china, when my Ma pushed the biscuit plate down the table. 'Michael, give Brenda another one.' If my Ma had been able to read my thoughts then she'd have had heart failure.

But the priest was the only one who was privy to them. 'Anything else, my son?' they always ask, but they know damn well there's something else, and they know it's not murder or you'd have blurted it out first thing, instead of treating them to the usual run-through of the lies and the bad words and the disobedience – that sorry wee poem you've been reciting since the age of seven. They know what it is you have to say, and that's what they've been waiting to hear and you've been keeping back until the end. Would it make it any easier, I wonder, if you did it the other way round? 'Bless me father, it's a fortnight since my last confession and I've been committing so many sins of impurity I'm nearly going blind...'

'With yourself, my son? Or with another?'

'With myself, father.'

But what I really wanted to tell him was that it had

been with Brenda. I wanted to confess that I'd gone up to her room one hot afternoon when we were the only two in the house; that she'd opened the door wearing nothing but a wraparound nightie; that the nightie had fallen open and we'd fallen into bed...

But I never got the chance, because Tom Canham beat me to it. The sales rep from Skegness, the Eric Morecambe lookalike who drove a Maxi and darned his own socks – he turned out to be an adulterer. I've not been able to take the word seriously since. *Adultery*, I read somewhere, and instead of Hollywood vamps and private eyes I think of Tom with a needle in one hand and the sole of a sock stretched over the other, and my Da taking the piss out of him, and Tom insisting that if you want a job done well you have to do it yourself. Hard to imagine him in bed with Brenda.

I wonder when my Ma rumbled them. She must have seen something we missed. Looking back there were a few giveaways: him jerking his hand away from her leg when I took in their dinner one night; his mug on her dressing table; one of them leaving the house always within a few minutes of the other. All innocent to me – which shows how innocent *I* was – until I overheard my Ma giving Tom a telling-off behind the sitting-room door.

'You and Brenda are big enough an' old enough to look after yourselves. And what ye do outside the house is none of my affair' – she's a great one for the unintentional pun – 'but I've got weans tae think of, so Ah don't want any carryin' on in here.' And it wasn't until then that I'd any idea they *had been* carrying on.

Carrying on is my Da prancing around in my Ma's housecoat, wearing the duster mop as a wig, doing his

Dick Emery impersonation for the visitors. But it's also Brenda and Tom at it, practising adultery, having SEX. The great unmentionable three-letter word.

Pregnant's another unmentionable, or it used to be. It seemed to be. When we were weans and my Ma and the aunties were sitting here gossiping round the range they found no end of alternatives to the word. An addition to the family. The pitter-patter of tiny feet. More wee cares on the way. Occasionally, we did overhear that someone was 'goin' tae have a baby', but we never heard that she was pregnant. Why not? It's the correct medical term for the state. But they wouldn't use it, at least not in front of us. They avoided it as coyly as my Ma does when she says *shog dite* for dog shite. *Preg–nant*. It's supposed to be a blessing, but they behaved as if it was a curse. And in Anne's case – in my Ma's eyes – I suppose it was.

Hard to believe that Anne and David have been married four years. March 1972 – not long after Bloody Sunday. It was pretty bloody in here, too. Every time I see those women in the Bogside banging their bin lids for the TV cameras, I think of David. My Ma and Da are at the front door, he's racing out the back, and he knocks the lid off the bin and sends it clanging down the yard.

Anne told me the other day they started going out when I was ten or eleven. He was probably too scared to come near the house in those days, and even if he had I wouldn't have remembered him. There were always boyfriends coming and going. Para was the only one who stuck out, and that's because he was black, the first black man we had ever seen. When he came to pick up Judette that first evening, our curiosity got the better of our shyness. We stared at the poor bugger. We couldn't believe the ebony sheen of his forehead, the contrasting pink of his palms. We did everything but prod him to check he was real. Peter looked at his Volkswagen and asked if all the men like him drove black cars. He took it well. 'He might be a darkie, but he's a lovely good-mannered fella,' my Ma said when he had gone. We boys thought so, too. It wasn't every boyfriend that gave us a tin of Quality Street each for Christmas.

I wonder what would have happened if he and Judette had stayed together... Would a mixed marriage of that kind be any harder than Anne and David's has been? Would black and white have a rougher time of it in this country than orange and green?

David says he's never been an Orangeman. But that's how he seemed to all of us. A Protestant who played the drums in a band on the Twelfth at a time when he was going out with a Catholic girl. Hardly a match made in heaven. Not much of a match in height, either. Anne's always complained that she can't wear high heels because she ends up towering over him. But when she's in flatties and he's in his platforms, with the hair feathered up like Rod Stewart's, they're roughly on a par. Except in my Ma and Da's eyes. They still have no time for David, though they don't make it as obvious as they used to.

Back then, every time his name was mentioned, my Ma would purse her lips and shake her head and my Da'd give that purple scowl. The rows I heard at night when I was dozing in the back house...

'Anne, this has got tae stop. There's no future in it for either of ye.'

'Look, dear. Ah know ye're fond o' 'im, but ye'll find somebody else.'

'Ah won't find somebody else. Ah don't *want* tae find somebody else.'

'Well, ye'll have tae, for this can't go on. Ah'm forbiddin' ye to have any more tae do wi' 'im.'

'Och, Daddy, don't be silly.'

'Don't you *dar*' talk tae me like that. Ye'll do as ye're damn well bid.'

'Mick, calm down, ye'll have the whole house awake.'

The voices fall; there's the sound of sniffing.

'Here, take this. Go on.'

'Ah don't want a hankie.'

'Anne, listen tae me...'

But Anne's stopped listening. I hear a chair scrape on the floor, the kitchen door open, the front door bang. Then my Da's chair and my Ma's loud whisper: 'Mick, *Mick*. Leave her be. She'll come back on her own when she's cooled off.'

I knew then that my Ma and Da didn't like David, but I wasn't sure why. It wasn't just because he was a Protestant. Derek was a Protestant, and they got on well with him. Was it because he was a Protestant who played in an Orange band? Did that make him 'a bitter wee man'? Was it because he 'loses the head completely when he has a wheen o' drinks in 'im'? I didn't know then and I couldn't ask. I'd eavesdropped on the prosecution, heard nothing from the defence. But I knew David wasn't welcome. He could come into our house only when my Ma and Da were out of it.

They were away at a wedding or something that

summer evening of '71. We were all crammed in here in the kitchen: Anne, David, Trish, Bredge, Sean and I. We were the provisional government, cocky and shaky at the same time. David was sitting smoking at one end of the table, Trish at the other, as if they hadn't a care in the world. But they kept the sash window open at the top, and every so often one of them would get up and fan an arm in front of it to clear the smoke. Anne was making a second cup of tea. Bredge was standing over there by the cupboard, driving a knife into a flat tin of homemade toffee and passing shards of it to Sean and me. James Taylor's *Mud Slide Slim and the Blue Horizon* was playing. Trish loved that LP. We were all singing along to it when Bredge jumped up and turned the volume right down.

'Shh! What's that?' She darted into the hall and then straight back into the kitchen.

'Anne, David. Quick! Mummy and Daddy's back.'

David shot out of his chair.

'Somebody empty those ashtrays.'

'Da–*vid*! Hurry UP!'

'Hang on. Ah haven't got mae fuckin' jacket.'

'Trish – you keep them talkin' at the front door.'

One arm in the jacket, David ran through the scullery, out the back door – and straight into the bin. 'Shit!' he shouted, and then he was gone.

How did I end up being the one who locked the gate behind him? No sooner had I done it and put the lid back on the bin than my Ma appeared beside me.

'Hello, Mummy, was it a good night?'

'Not as noisy as the one ye seem tae have been havin' here. What are you pair o' boys doin' up at this time? And what was all that racket?'

'Ah was just throwin' out a load o' rubbish, and Ah knocked the lid off the bin.'

She cocked her head on one side and gave me a tell-me-another-one look.

'Are ye sure that's all ye were doin'?'

'Aye.'

She didn't ask me any more, and if she had I couldn't have explained. I was a conspirator, but I wasn't sure why. At that stage I knew only part of the plot.

Nineteen

It would have been six or seven months later that I was standing here by the range with that pair of David's trousers in my hand. Anne had passed them on in a carrier bag. 'Here, Michael. See if these are any use tae ye. David doesn't wear them any more.' Dark-brown flares with turn-ups. I've never been keen on brown, but beggars can't be choosers, and they were as good as new. They wouldn't even need turning up, for my legs were already as long as David's. I reckoned that if my Ma put a quick tuck in the waist I could be wearing them at Mass on Sunday.

I was holding them in front of me to see how they hung when I slipped a hand into the right-hand pocket and felt it. At first I thought it was a packet of chewing gum. I pulled it out. I knew then that Anne hadn't checked the pockets before she gave me the trousers.

I remember thinking how much it looked like an Elastoplast packet, except that it was thicker, more padded, flat at the edges, raised in the middle, as if there was some giant paper-clip inside. But they don't write that on paper-clips, do they? DUREX, DUREX, DUREX, Featherlite, Featherlite, Featherlite. It felt sinful just to be holding it.

I shouldn't have panicked. I should have shoved it in my pocket and got it out somewhere to have a good look at it when I had a bit of peace. Then the next time Chinner and the rest of them started boasting about French Ticklers I'd have been able to tell them that I preferred Featherlites. But when are you ever going to get peace in this house? Just imagine, there I am in the back return, chair wedged against the door, rolling the Durex on. And next thing I know my Ma's banging on the door saying she needs the room for somebody.

'Come on. I have tae get them beds stripped and the floor hoovered. What are ye doin' in there, anyway?'

I should have put it in my pocket. I just thought, Fuck, if she catches me with this all hell'll break loose. It'll be 'WhatinunderGod is this house comin' to?' and 'Where did ye get it anyway?' And Anne and David would have been in deep shit. So when I heard her slippers on the tiles I lifted the kettle and dropped the packet in the fire. Flames licking rubber – that was the last I saw of it.

'What are ye at, darlin'?'

'The fire's gettin' low. Ah was just givin' it a wee poke. Have ye got much to do the night?'

'Why?'

'D'ye think ye'd have time to put a tuck in these trousers for me?'

She took them from me and held them out, rubbing the material the way she does between the thumb and forefinger of her right hand. 'Not a bad bit o' cloth. Where did ye get them?'

'David gave me them.'

'Ah see,' she said, as if trousers might be as dodgy as the Trojan horse. 'Well, it'd be a shame, Ah suppose, tae let them go tae waste...an' we can't very well turn down a handout from yer sister's husband.'

And that was it: the closest thing to an official announcement I'm ever likely to hear from my Ma. Anne and David were married.

As if we needed to be told. Sean and I would have had to be pretty stupid not to cobble the story together for ourselves. No matter how innocent you are, you can't help noticing when one of your sisters moves out of the house.

'Mummy, what was Anne packin' for this mornin'? Where's she goin'?' Sean asked that day as we ate our tea.

My Ma looked up from her plate and glanced at my Da. 'She's movin' into a wee flat of her own down the street. She's a growin' girl and she wants a bit o' independence.'

'Aye, growin's the word,' my Da said, without looking up.

'Is it a nice flat?'

'Not nearly as nice as the room she has here, but she seems happy tae be payin' good money for it.'

'Can we go an' see 'er?'

'Well...' My Ma looked at my Da again. 'Ah'm sure ye can in a wee while, but ye'll have tae give 'er a chance tae get settled in.'

A chance to get settled in, a chance to get over the

morning sickness. Oh yeah, we boys weren't supposed to know about that, any more than we were supposed to hear my Ma promising to knit a cardie for the wean. Sean didn't believe me when I told him that.

'She's goin' tae have a baby? But she's not even married...'

By that stage she was, of course, but as it was done with shotguns rather than silver service we weren't invited. All right, *nobody* was invited, but at least the girls were told about it. I can understand about the pregnancy – my Ma and Da were ashamed that our sister was up the chute and they didn't want us blabbing it all over the Harbour Hill. But why couldn't they tell us about the wedding? Once it was over, anyway? Why did they leave us to figure out for ourselves that our sister was married? We wouldn't have heard a word about it if we hadn't gone round the house with our ears tuned like satellite dishes.

It was Judette and Derek who let slip the last few lines of the story, when they thought there was nobody else around to hear: 'I feel so sorry for Anne. It's supposed tae be the happiest day o' yer life. The white dress, the reception, the photos an' all the rest o' it. An' what does she get? She has tae sneak in the back door o' the chapel, wi' nobody tae watch her but you an' me.'

'Ah know. Ah was nearly cryin' maesel'.'

Judette had the works, of course, later in the year: the white dress, all the girls apart from Anne as bridesmaids, the piper piping; Danny and Peter cute in their waist-coats; and Sean and me looking mannish in our new navy blazers and grey flannels.

Eddie wasn't so mannish, or so Uncle Jimmy thought.

'Who's that tall lassie in the trouser suit?' somebody asked him.

'Where?'

'Over there – the wan wi' 'er back tae us.'

'Some lassie. That's the best man. An' the hair's nearly as straggly on 'is chin as it is on 'is collar.'

They made an odd pair: Derek as neat and anonymous as a bank clerk; Eddie like Robinson Crusoe pressed into a suit and itching to get back to the beach. Derek's family looked even more uncomfortable. At least Eddie had been through the rehearsal, he knew what to expect. But they didn't – it was probably the first time they'd ever darkened the door of a Catholic church. They'd still be on their feet a second or two after everybody else had sat down, or sitting when everybody else had hit the kneeling boards, and then Derek's brother or his wife would spot they were out of line and start tugging at trousers or coat-tails.

Easy for me to laugh; I wouldn't have any more idea what to do if roles were reversed. I'd love to go into a Methodist or Church of Ireland service just to see what they do, how they run things. But there's no way you could do that in Portstewart without word of it getting back to my Ma. Journalistic curiosity, I might say, but she'd be bound to think that David had been getting at me and trying to convert me. Not that he goes too often himself; and he seems to know little more about what goes on in the Orange Hall than I do. He might be Orange in our eyes, but he's not an Orangeman in theirs. He's sold out, shacked up with a Catholic, so he doesn't belong. And Anne's caught between him and my Ma and Da: David insisting that the kids go to his church; my Ma and Da insisting that they're going to finish up good wee Catholics even if they've had a bad start.

Poor Anne. It was ages after she moved out before she came near the house again. When she did pop in that afternoon for a cuppa, Peter and Danny were all over her.

'Anne's here. Anne's here. Are ye havin' a baby, Anne? When are ye comin' back, Anne?'

'Aye, Anne's here,' my Ma said, coming out of the scullery with a sheet in her hand. 'We were beginnin' tae think she'd forgotten where we lived.'

'Ah'm not the only one wi' a short memory,' Anne said. 'It's not as if *my* door's barred.'

She met my Ma in the middle of the kitchen and pulled at one end of the sheet. My Ma jerked it away at first, and then she saw Anne looking all hurt, so she let her draw it out, and they both walked backwards so they could stretch it lengthways. Jerk. Thwack. Jerk. Thwack. It was as if they were saying something with the sheet that they couldn't put into words. And then they stepped closer again to fold it, and they were both smiling and trying not to cry at the same time.

'Bredge, make us a wee drap o' tay,' my Ma said.

'Naw, I'll do it,' Anne said.

'Ye will not,' my Ma said. 'Ye'll sit on yer backside. A wumman in your condition should be puttin' 'er feet up every chance she gets.'

The tea came and went, and the small talk with it.

'Well, Anne,' my Ma said, 'how are ye feelin'?'

'Ah'm fine. Just a wee bit sick in the mornin's.'

'Aye, well. Ye can't say ye weren't warned. It was you made yer bed. Now ye have tae lie in it.'

'Ah know that, Mummy. Ah won't need remindin' again.'

My Ma nodded.

Anne started coming round regularly after that, but it was a while before David decided it was safe to come with her. I can't blame him. I was away that first time he came over, but the second time was bad enough. I was sitting here with my Ma and Da and their smiles were as warm as the light in a freezer.

'Hello, Anne. Hello, David,' my Ma said.

'How ye doin', Mrs Kerr, Mick,' David said.

My Da was sitting smoking in his chair at the head of the table. He took a fit of coughing that saved him giving any response but a wave of his hand.

More chairs were pulled out, the teapot went on, the formalities were observed. But that's all they were: formalities. There was none of the chat there usually is over a cuppa. It didn't even feel like our kitchen. My Ma, with her hands clasped in her lap, might have been sitting in the dining room, waiting for the verdict of some tourist-board inspector. David searched in a pocket for his fags and then thought better of lighting up. He started fidgeting with the hair over his ears. My Da shot him a look that said he'd like to take him up the Prom this minute and get him under Johnny Stevenson's clippers.

Every remark ran into a dead end.

'It's cooled down a lot, hasn't it?'

'Aye, it has.'

'Are ye busy at work, Daddy?'

'Aye, fairly.'

'How's yer mother, David?'

'She's rightly, thanks.'

After five minutes, my Da had had enough. When Anne went to top up his mug, he said: 'Naw, no more for me. I'm just nipping out for a wee while.' Off he went to the Splash, and he didn't ask David to go with him.

For a while he wasn't too keen on sharing a drink with Tom Canham, either. He and my Ma were pissed off with Tom *and* Brenda. Not only were the two of them having an affair, but they'd been egging on Anne and David. At least that's the way my Ma and Da saw it. Anne says that's balls, but it is true that Tom and Brenda were the only adults at the time who had a kind word to say to her and David. They treated them like a couple of young lovers rather than a couple of sinners. If it hadn't been for Tom, they'd have had nowhere to spend their honeymoon; he lent them his flat near the Strand.

Of course, we boys didn't even know at the time that he had a flat. We didn't even know he was still in Portstewart. When my Ma said he was going we assumed she meant back to Skegness – not to a flat at the other end of the town so he could screw Brenda without having somebody tell him he shouldn't be doing it.

But it's all over now. She's back with her husband, Tom's dead of a heart attack, and when my Da talks about him it's always as one of his old bosom buddies.

That's hardly the way he feels about David, but at least these days he'll have a drink with him, even if he's always moaning that he's tight. Which isn't true, anyway. Everybody says he's always the last to buy a round, but he's generous enough to me. I go down to the flat to give him back that Bob Dylan *Greatest Hits* album and he says,

'Naw, you hang on to it. I'm gettin' a bit sick of it anyway.' And I know he isn't.

At least we can go to the flat now without pretending we're going somewhere else; without feeling we're being disloyal. There's a good one: disloyal Catholics.

'Where have you been?' my Ma used to say.

'Aw, just down the Prom.' Just down the Prom to my black-sheep sister's flat.

That must have been the first flat I was ever in; it had never occurred to me that people lived above the shops on the Prom. Anne would be there, the bump getting bigger by the day – though that probably had as much to do with her homemade caramel squares as it did with the baby. She'd show us the curtains she'd made, the bed they'd bought, the table and chairs she was about to order. They were all out of the Freemans' catalogue, all being paid off in monthly instalments. But Sean and I never thought of that. You don't, do you, when you're fourteen and twelve? You just think, Our house is full of stuff from auctions, and Anne and David are buying everything new.

Anne would be showing off her knitting: the cardies, the booties, the doll-sized jumpers. But I was more interested in David's stereo and his Gram Parsons albums and the great view you got from the window over the Prom. I didn't even think of the baby, didn't think there might be more rows after it was born. I was blundering about with my tongue as well as my feet. I remember looking round the flat that night, envying Anne and David their new TV and their stereo and their independence.

'Ye know, Anne, you're really lucky,' I told her.

She smiled. 'Do ye think so, Michael? Do ye really think so?'

Twenty

I don't think so now. I'd hate to have gone through what she has – torn between parents and boyfriend and now between parents and husband. David insists there's no way Karen's going to be christened a Catholic, and my Ma and Da insist there's no way she's going to be anything else, so the kid gets taken to the chapel behind David's back. (I wonder whether it occurred to the priest to ask where the happy father was...) Then David gets tanked up and comes tearing in here, effing and blinding, telling my Ma she's an interfering oul' bitch, and I'm wondering what the hell's going on, because I'd no idea either that there'd been a christening. He's a wild man when he has drink in him, and he said some awful things to my Ma; but how would I have felt if I'd been in his shoes? I wouldn't have been too pleased – with either my mother-in-law or my wife.

It's like the in-laws from hell. David's folks were no keener on having Anne in their family than my Ma and Da were on having him. They've mellowed a bit, but they're still not delirious about the way things have gone. When the granny tut-tuts over what Anne's cooked for her beloved grandson, it's not just domestic comedy; there's an edge. It's a Protestant granny disapproving of Catholic cooking. Poor Anne. After everything else, she finds they're so pushed for somewhere to live when they move out of the flat that they have to move in with the granny.

And here am I grumbling about losing a room for a couple of nights! What must it have been like for the girls when we were all sharing the back house, with Sean and me peeking over the blankets as they undressed? And sometimes they were three in a bed – at least we had a bunk each. Me on top, him down below. That's the only way any of us has ever slept *under* a bed. That poor wee bugger in Belfast is probably still doing it, every night of the week.

But Belfast, as my Ma used to tell the visitors, is a long way off. You believe it, too, if you're from Belfast yourself, because you want to believe it. You're part of the conspiracy to lengthen and broaden this cramped wee place. You stretch it in your mind, so that it's no longer – what? – barely 85 miles from top to bottom and 110 miles wide. It's ten, twenty times that size. It's as big as Texas, as big as Alaska.

It looks different, of course, from England, Scotland and Wales. They've no interest there in making myths out of maps. It must have been as early as '70 or '71 that even the old faithfuls gave up on us. 'Dear Mrs Kerr, After spending so many happy holidays in Portstewart, I am sorry to say that we will not be coming over this year, but I'm sure you can understand why...' She could. She'd stand out there at the front gate, she and Mrs Nicholl and Mrs Paul, chewing it over and commiserating with one another.

'Ye can't blame them, can ye?'

'Not at all, dear. We know what it's like. We know there's no bother here.'

'But they don't. How could they? If ye're over there watchin' the news, lookin' at them maps, ye're bound to think the whole place has taken leave of its senses.'

They had a point. We do live in a different country up here. To see it, you've only got to look at Dominic Rafferty and those other wee wankers on our bus in the morning, off to a Catholic school and waving their tartan scarves around. They think tartan's cool; they've no bloody idea it's the badge of gangs in Belfast who *murder* Catholics.

We know little about our own country and we've seen less. I've been nowhere because I've spent all my summers in a boarding house, but I'm sure most of the guys I've been through St Joseph's with aren't much better travelled. I think of Mrs McWilliams that day in English instructing us on the niceties of letter writing, and that question somebody asked her for a laugh: 'Please, Miss, when you're giving your address, do you put County Derry or Londonderry?'

'Well,' she said with a wee smile, 'that depends...If you're writing to a friend, there's no harm in putting Derry. If you're applying for a job, on the other hand, you might find it more profitable to put Londonderry.' As if we didn't know.

But that's all Derry was to us – the county we lived in. Most of us had never been anywhere near the city, let alone to Belfast ('So you're from Belfast,' they said at the interview, as if it was the only inhabited place in the Province). But we still prided ourselves on being men of the world, or at least of the town. We took the piss out of Flappers and Peter Doherty because they left ten minutes earlier than we did to get their bus home. 'Yes, Miss,' we told that cute Mademoiselle Hannelly in French class, 'them country boys have to get back before it's dark, for there's no electricity where they live.' As if Articlave and Castlerock were in the boondocks, instead of up the road from Coleraine.

I did the same in Morelli's takeout with Seamus Quigg and Brian Canning, aping the voices of those farmers who'd come down to the Port for the Big Sunday. ('Shahurrah' Sunday is how everybody says it, but I've never seen it written down. I wonder where it came from, how it should be spelt...) My Ma remembers when it really was Big, when people would say to themselves, September's over, winter's coming, this is our last chance for a day out by the seaside. And they'd pour in from every corner of the country.

That was long over by the time I started in Morelli's, but we still got the odd old farmer rolling in, so we had to be ready for the way they talked. 'Yonny hemburgers? Yonny hemburgers?' Quigg had hardly finished sending them up when that guy came in and said it exactly that way, and we were trying so hard not to laugh that we had to run to the back of the shop and leave the other Seamus to serve him.

He was a nice guy, Seamus, and his only vice seemed

to be Brylcreem. He put enough on his hair every day to fry a fish supper. He was a big softie, let us get away with murder. Unlike Alex. Mind you, she got me the job in the first place, or at least told my Ma there was one going. 'It'll be the life o' ye,' says my Ma. 'About time ye were earnin' a crust at weekends instead o' footerin' about at fishin' and football.' So she marches me off to see Audrey the secretary, squeezed in at her desk between the boxes of cones and the wages envelopes, and next weekend I'm salting, peppering and wrapping fish suppers at 16p an hour.

That was a bit like setting a fire – easy once you'd been shown how. The number of times I sent people out with paper flapping and chips dropping all over the shop... Then Seamus the Bryl gave me a demonstration. Pull wad of greaseproof paper towards you, so that it sits diagonally across counter. Salt and vinegar the chips. Push carton a bit more than a carton's width in from the corner of paper nearest you. Fold corner in over carton. Fold right edge in, left edge in, as if you're making an envelope, then roll the carton over and over till you get to the end of the paper. It's a doddle.

Why did they close the takeout? Never overly busy, I suppose, and there was competition from the Superfry and McClure's. So off I went to help do the ice-cream in the coffee bar.

I used to be mortified when Siobhan McKenna and Rosanna Morelli came in. One of them at a time was bad enough; why did they have to come as a pair? I suppose I was still a bit soft on Siobhan even then. Maybe I still am. Why could I never pluck up the courage to ask her out? There was Dick at thirteen already going round the cliff walk with his hands all over Angela Whatshername and I hadn't got beyond sending Siobhan the anonymous Valentine card. And she thought it was from Michael Harvey anyway. And I was too shy to put her right. Everybody knew I fancied her – even the teachers. Kevin Bradley did anyway. Him and his ha-ha line about her Da being a butcher: 'So, Michael, is it true that you're getting free meat these days . . .?'

No danger of me ending up with free ice-cream, though. I like Rosanna, but I've never really fancied her. I just hated her seeing me in that blue nylon jacket behind the counter, one of the Morelli family's employees. There she was, somebody I'd been to primary school with, and I was depending on a job with her uncle for my pocket money.

I wonder if Alex's radar picked up any of that. There wasn't much she missed. She kept that place as tightly controlled as the curls in her blue rinse, but she was easier on me than she was on Stephen Donnelly; maybe she still saw in me the baby she nursed when she was living two doors down. She was forever ticking him off for being late or having his hair in his eyes or making messy wafers. 'How do ye expect the poor lady to eat that without it drippin' all over 'er? Here, let me fix it.'

She always caught him, too, when he was taking the piss out of kids from Belfast. They found him scary enough just to look at, soaring above them in platforms even higher than mine, like some stilt man in a circus.

'Can I have a poke, please?'

'A what?'

'A poke.'

'Ye want me tae give ye a poke?'

209

'Naw, not *give* me wan. Ah've got the money an' all.'

'Ye mean ye're goin' tae pay – '

And then Alex would appear at his elbow, with that don't-you-dare-bugger-about look. 'Yes, son, of course you can have a poke. This boy here doesn't know that poke is a Belfast word for cone, but he'll soon learn – *won't you, Stephen?* – if he wants to carry on workin' here.'

Poke for cone, slider for wafer. Sometimes they speak a different language, and even when they're speaking ours they make it harsher, harder; a sound in keeping with a place where they have bombs. We don't have any of that here. Or so we thought until the one in Coleraine.

Hard to believe that was only three years ago, and that six people were killed. If we'd known any of them their names would be mentioned now and again: 'Aye, poor so-and-so, God rest him,' my Ma would say. But we didn't, so we've put it behind us, almost as if we don't want to remember it; as if we don't want to be reminded that 'all that nonsense', as my Ma calls it, is not so far from home as we like to pretend. I wonder if Bredge ever thinks of it, if she sees it as a nightmare she's avoided having again by going to Australia. She was in a hell of a state when she got home that day.

She'd come four miles on the bus, and it was as if she was still passing the scene of it. 'There was glass all over the place and people runnin' about with blood pourin' from their faces. I saw this woman with awful cuts and she was tryin' to calm this wee girl beside her and the wee girl was tuggin' at her arm and screamin' her head off. An' our driver was sayin' all the way down the road, "How could anybody in their right mind do somethin' like this?" He was nearly cryin' himsel'.'

She was still shaking as my Ma cuddled her. 'It's all right, love. Ye're home now. Ye're safe.'

There's a part of me that wishes our bus had gone the same way as hers and I'd seen what she saw. You can't say that to people without having them think you're bonkers, but you can't help thinking it, wondering what it's like. If I had seen something like that I'd have a better reason for going to London, for giving up on the whole fucking country. I'd have something to tell the other students, too. After all they've heard about life in Northern Ireland, they're going to find me a terrible disappointment.

I didn't even understand until I got home what I'd seen in the assembly hall. There we were, two or three verses into 'Soul Of My Saviour', when the curtains went swinging halfway up the wall like giant windscreen wipers. Nudge and a wink to Dick: 'Maybe God's tellin' us He doesn't like the singin'.' Then, when I heard Bredge's story, it clicked – the curtains must have been lifted by the shock waves of the blast coming towards us from Railway Road. And what had we been doing only minutes earlier? Praying for peace.

'Please, God, let our two communities in Northern Ireland learn to live in harmony. Lord hear us. Lord graciously hear us.'

Or, as Jimmy Young used to put it, 'Will ye's for God's sake stop fightin'.'

Our Jimmy, late every Saturday night, sending up the bigotry of both sides and making us laugh at ourselves. Well, some of us were laughing, anyway. You can only assume the rest of Victoria Terrace found it as funny as we did. It must have been good – my Da came back early from the pub just to watch it, fish suppers from McClure's steaming in his hands.

I'd never heard of Jimmy Young till then, though he's obviously been around a long time. Must be at least fifty. A bee sting of a nose, wide fleshy lips; if Liberace had a poor Irish cousin this is what he'd look like. Come to think of it, that was the theme of one of the shows – the Yanks' obsession with their ancestry. A pair of them arrive looking for an Ireland that no longer exists, but which they're prepared to pay good money to see, so the sharp folk of Belfast put them on a play and diddle them out of their dollars.

Jimmy didn't spare the English, either. Those two English guys in the cast were sometimes soldiers, sometimes officials and sometimes journalists, but they were always clueless. Apart from them and the woman playing that wee scrounger Emily Beattie, who never took her curlers out, it was a one-man show. Jimmy was the mammy's boy, the drunk, the granny from Ballymena, the union leader. And he was Orange Lily, the harridan who even had the Union Jack on her knickers.

'Isn't Lily great?' I said to Dick that day in class when the series had been running a couple of weeks.

'Yeah,' he said, 'but Mrs O'Rally's good, too.'

'Yeah, she is,' I said, not knowing who the hell he was talking about and being too cowardly to admit it.

So I watched more closely the following Saturday night, and I realized that Mrs O'Rally was Lily's Catholic counterpart – not so loud, maybe, not so visible, but every bit as ignorant. She was the sort of woman who'd turn down a blood transfusion for fear it might be Protestant; for fear it would have her writing 'Fuck the Pope' on gable ends.

So how come Dick saw that at the outset and I didn't? Maybe it's family circumstances. Maybe, because his Ma used to be a Prod and turned to marry his Da, they're better able in his house to see things from both sides. And maybe we can't really do that, no matter how much we think we can. But Anne and David's kids should be able to, for they'll be a bit of both themselves. Maybe they'll have it in their features, too, and fox all those eejits who think they can tell a Catholic from a Protestant by the look of the face.

Twenty-One

'Protestant-lookin'.' That's one of Maisie's favourite phrases. She goes into the breakfast room, handbag dangling from a bony arm. She stops by the settee, about to sit down, then shakes her head. Setting down the handbag, she pulls the cover from the settee, smooths out its wrinkles and drapes it back. She lifts the cushions in turn, plumps them up, and puts one against each armrest, one in the middle and one against the back. 'There,' she says, easing her bottom into her favourite corner by the fire, 'that's a wee bit more Protestant-lookin'.' It's her joke, her response to what she imagines is their view of us: that we're as careless of mess as we are of contraception.

She knows we're as good as them – or at least she is. She's never done giving us highlights from the CV: first pupil to register at St Colum's; first pupil at the Convent and, in nineteen hundred and whenever, its first head girl;

and first woman in the British Isles to hold a public service vehicle licence. She trots all this out as if we're hearing it for the first time, as if four years haven't passed since she arrived at our front door in emerald cardigan, black skirt and stockings the colour of strong tea.

My Da gets fed up listening to her, but he only has himself to blame. He asked her in. There she was, nursing her half pint of stout in the Anchor – she's probably still getting it free because her old boy used to own the place – when he got chatting to her. Her landlady was selling up and Maisie would soon have nowhere to live. 'Don't you worry, Maisie,' I can hear him saying, 'while I have a roof over mae own head Ah'll not see you on the street.'

Having had a few, of course, he completely forgot what he'd said. The first thing my Ma heard of the arrangement was when Maisie arrived to finalize it. Maisie wasn't going to be steered away, either, though my Ma says she did make an effort. 'Mrs McCann, ye know you might be better movin' in with Mr an' Mrs Tully. The pair of them's retired and they don't make a lot o' noise. I've four growin' boys in this house an' Ah'm not sure how you and they'll get on...'

'I'm well used wi' boys,' Maisie told her. 'Sure haven't Ah spent mae life nursin' boys *and* girls. The boys an' me'll get on the best. Now, where's this room?'

Maisie wasn't daft. There was none of the horse-trading there would have been with Mrs Tully. All she had to say was, 'I'm not a moneyed woman, ye know, Mrs Kerr, Ah can only give ye nine pounds a week,' and my Ma rolled over.

Nine pounds a week for bed, breakfast, dinner, tea and

supper! Not to mention endless supplies of tea and biscuits! My Ma's far too soft. She always has been. The number of times I've seen her standing by this cupboard totting up bills and then scoring things out, refusing payment for this or that... 'Supper, dear? Sure ye only had a sandwich or two. It's not worth botherin' about... An' Ah won't charge ye for the wee boy, for all he ate wouldn't fill a robin.' The idea of her running a shop is laughable – nearly as mad as Securicor putting my Da in a uniform and sending him out to guard the Strand Hotel for those couple of months, when he wasn't fit enough to climb a ladder, let alone chase burglars. But of course none of us laughed when she suggested it. She was so sure she could make a go of it. I suppose she looked at Sally in Limavady and thought, If my sister can do it there then I can do it here.

She was lucky with the location – there's no shortage of people coming and going on that corner of the Diamond – and the shop itself was a reasonable size and in decent shape. At least it was after she and Anne had spent a few days' elbow grease on it. Whoever the last tenants were, cleaning wasn't one of their strong points.

She was so chuffed that day she opened, standing there at the ready behind her very own counter. 'Well? What d'ye think o' our wee shop?'

What I thought was that it looked amateurish, old-fashioned, the sort of place I'd want to keep my friends away from in case they laughed at it. Cabinets were still empty; there were car-sized spaces on some of the shelves between one lot of tins or packets and the next. It looked like we couldn't afford to stock it properly. It looked like a shop that was about to close.

But I made the right noises. I told her we'd soon be as big a chain as Crazy Prices. If goodwill was any substitute for capital, we might have been. We'd certainly have lasted a few years rather than a few months. 'Good on ye, Mrs Kerr, Ah hope ye do well,' people would tell her. 'May your till be always janglin'.' Some of the same people made sure that the till stayed silent when it should have been jangling.

'Och, Ah'm so stupid. Ah've come out without mae purse. Can Ah pay ye themorra?'

'Oh, dear. Ah'm fifty pee short. Is it all right if Ah call back wi' it later?'

And more often than not my Ma let them away with it, just as she let Maisie away with her nine pounds a week.

She's not much to look at, Maisie: hardly five foot, a bag of bones, skin on her neck loose as a turkey's. One wee puff, you'd think, would blow her over. But there's determination in those milky eyes. It was no time at all before she'd claimed that seat in the corner of the breakfast room as her own, and she never moves from it except at her convenience. Mornings are for strolling the Prom, evenings for bingo, bridge and whist. In between, she's jammed in that corner, pipe-cleaner legs splayed, nose buried in a Regency romance from the library or the *Daily Mirror* crossword.

'Seven down. "Decades and decades". Seven letters beginning with C. What would that be?'

'Centuries, Maisie, which is how long it seems you've been here.'

'What's that?'

'I said "Centuries".'

'Aye. Just what I was goin' tae put. Now, where was Ah...Eleven across. "James Bond has one to kill." L.I.C.E.N.C.E. Which reminds me...did Ah ever tell ye I was the first woman bus driver in the British Isles?'

And off she goes on the story of the wagon the family ran between the Anchor and Coleraine, ferrying the shift workers from home to factory, and how her brother Tom wasn't well one night and she volunteered to drive.

'Well, the bus had tae be crank-started, an' by the time Ah got it goin' mae arm really hurt. But Ah made the journey tae Coleraine anyway. An' when Ah got back Ah went tae Hopefield Hospital for a check-up. An' d'ye know what they said...'

Of course I bloody know; she's never done telling me.

'...the arm was broken.'

There have been times, I'm sure, when my Ma would like to have broken both of them, if only to stop her scattering her fag ash over the carpet. She doesn't seem to notice that cigarettes produce ash. An inch of grey builds up on the end of her ciggie, she moves her head, or gives one of those wheezing coughs, and it goes all over herself and the carpet.

'Ye should tell 'er,' my Da says to my Ma.

'Ah couldn't do that.'

'Well, Ah'll tell 'er, then.'

'Ye will not. Don't you say a word.'

So Sean and I get lumbered with dropping the heavy hints. Up she gets, padding towards the door. And over we go straight away with the fireside shovel and the brush. If she notices, she pays no heed. She's no more inclined to change her ways than she is her seat.

She gets so pissed off if she comes in and finds Elizabeth in that corner. They might both be boarders, but Maisie's in no doubt that there's a pecking order and she's on top. She says nothing, but she doesn't need to. She looks at Elizabeth and wrinkles her nose as if a stink bomb's gone off. Elizabeth pretends she can't smell it.

But Maisie won't suffer in silence if she finds the last few clues of her crossword filled in.

'Who's been at this?'

'I don't know. One o' the boys?'

'Huh. There's been none o' the boys in this room the day.'

'Well ye needn't be lookin' at me. I never touched yer oul' crossword.'

She's always telling us these stories about the scrapes she got into when she did her nursing training, and now she's in her dotage she's got the cheek to call Elizabeth 'that flighty wee thing'. Elizabeth's hardly that. She's out at night less often than Maisie is. Unless she's seeing Johnny or going home to the glen for the weekend, she's likely to be sitting here with the rest of us watching the box. Just what her mother ordered, I'm sure, when she left her here, in the firm trust that she would not only be fed and watered but watched over and guided. My Ma's not just Elizabeth's landlady; she's her guardian angel.

Now and then you hear the angel delivering holy writ: 'Now, Elizabeth, it's not my place...but you've been startin' tae keep late nights...Ah'm sure yer Mammy wouldn't be happy...'

But it doesn't happen often. Elizabeth, in my Ma's view, is 'a good sensible wee girl'. Except, of course, when she's winding up Maisie. That's never hard; Maisie gets seriously pissed off if anyone interferes with those niceties she sees as her right, those confirmations of her status as paying guest. Like the bone-china cup and saucer.

At first my Ma wasn't going to play along the other night. When Elizabeth lifted the cup from Maisie's supper tray, and swapped it for that Man United mug with the chip out of the rim, my Ma told her to put it back.

'Och, Mrs Kerr, don't be a spoilsport. Ah'm only havin' a laugh.'

'Go on, then. But ye'd better make yerself scarce, for she won't be a bit pleased.'

Maisie had carried the tray into the breakfast room before she noticed the mug, and by that time Elizabeth was halfway up the stairs. But she'd have heard all right what was hollered after her through the banisters. 'Ye wee BITCH. Ah know rightly it was you did this.'

We don't know, and we'll never know, who put the note through the shop letterbox telling my Ma that it would be good for her health if she stayed closed during the Loyalist Workers' Strike. But the chances are it was somebody who had been in and out of the shop; probably one of those boys who had wished her luck when she opened. I wonder if it crossed his mind that the last sort of luck she needed was the loss of a day's trade...Even if it had, things would have been no different. It was a blanket ban; everybody running a business on either side of the house was getting a note, and there couldn't be any concessions – certainly not to a Catholic. So while my Ma was rattled, she knew she wasn't alone in being rattled. She knew it wasn't personal.

The barracking Trish and Keith got was different; that *was* personal, and it was one of the things that led to them breaking up. Would she have even thought of going to Australia if they'd stayed together? Maybe not. I don't know whether she was in love with him, but I know she was very fond of him. We all liked him, too. 'He's a lovely fella, Keith,' my Ma would say. 'A lovely well-mannered fella.' As well he might be, being the son of a Presbyterian minister. When he put on that black polo neck you might have taken him for a cleric himself – if he hadn't worn it with those loons. The flares on them were a good few inches wider than the ones I've got on now. The whole outfit made him look even taller than he was, so when he went out to the Imp you thought he'd have to fold himself in two to get into the driving seat.

He had to do a lot of mileage in that car. I think Trish was still living at home when they started going out, so it was easy then as he was staying over the road, working in the bank down the Prom. Then, when she started college in Belfast, he'd be picking her up from her digs on a Friday and running her back on the Sunday and sometimes going to Larne as well to see his mother. From what my Ma says, his mother wasn't keen on the relationship. She liked Trish well enough, but she was worried that Keith would be given a hard time in Larne if word got around that he was seeing a Catholic. They were both ready for that; what they weren't expecting was to be given a hard time in Portstewart.

Trish was still crying when she came back that night. 'Trish, what on earth's the matter?' my Ma asked her. 'Nothin'.'

'Some nothin'. The tears are trippin' ye. Have you and

Keith had a row?'

'No.'

'Then what is it?'

And then, in between sobs, Trish blurted it out. 'Ah've just been called all the names o' the day up the Prom.'

'By who?'

'By John Rodgers. An' his brother.'

'What did they say?'

'They said I was an effin' Fenian bitch and that Keith was a disgrace for bein' seen with me and weren't there enough decent women for him in the country that he had to make a fool o' himself by chasin' after the likes o' me. An' everybody was turnin' round tae look at us 'cause they were makin' so much noise.'

'And where's Keith now?' my Ma asked.

'He's in the house,' Trish said. 'He was goin' tae go an' have it out with them but I told him it was silly. They're only a couple o' oul' drunks and they probably won't even remember they said it in the mornin'.'

'They are. An' Ah wouldn't give them the satisfaction o' seein' ye upset.'

'Ah didn't. Ah didn't start cryin' till Ah was nearly in the door.'

It can't have been long after that that Trish and Keith split up. 'It's a shame,' my Ma said. 'I was very fond o' Keith, too. But they both decided it was for the best.'

Did they now? Wouldn't it be more honest to say that others decided for them? The way they do so often in this bloody country.

The same was true when Trish and Bredge made up their minds to go to Australia. Yes, they'd heard a lot from Derek and Judy about the jobs and the sun and the social life, so in that sense it was a decision they made themselves, and for positive reasons. But they weren't just going away to start a new life; they were going away to put an old one behind them. They were like all those poor buggers who ran away from the famine, except that they were running away from the bigots.

The house has never seemed so empty as it did that afternoon. Even Maisie made herself scarce, as if she felt she was intruding on grief. 'Mrs Kerr, Ah'm goin' out for mae wee walk,' she said, when everybody knew damn well that she never went walking at that time of the day.

'Come on – enough o' them long faces,' my Da said. 'They can write. They can phone. An' before ye know it they'll be back on holiday. An' hasn't Patricia had the best o' starts?'

My Ma stopped crying long enough to agree to that. What better omen could there be than for Trish to pass her driving test six hours before she was due to get on the plane – especially when the examiner was the oul' bugger who'd failed her the first time?

Twenty-Two

I knew I was going to fail A-level Religious Studies long before I got anywhere near the examination room. I blame Sister Joan. And so will everybody else, since I had no trouble at all with the English Lit or the French. Thank God I only need those two to get into college.

Maybe they thought I was a bit of a holy Joe when it came up at the interview. 'You're taking an A-level in Religious Studies; that's an unusual choice...' For a minute I thought of spinning them a line, telling them that I hoped it would help me to understand the divisions between the two communities in Northern Ireland. But I chickened out and told them the truth, which probably did me even more credit. Poor boy, the choice of subjects was so limited at his school that when he was casting round for a third A-level he had no option but to do Religious Studies.

It certainly wasn't because I enjoyed the company of Sister Joan. There *are* a few nuns who can leave the convent in the morning without dabbing Sanctimony under their chins. Fairy Feet's one of them: hardly as tall as the first-year girls, but with a huge sense of fun. But Sister Joan's one of the old guard, a Pharisee in female form.

I can't get this picture out of my head of her chasing us round that retreat centre in the dark when we were about fourteen. She still had the full penguin suit on, so whoever knocked on her door must have done it when she was at her devotions. There am I, back in my cell, standing on a chair looking through the fanlight to see where the other guys have gone. I swivel my head slowly, pressing it against the glass, and who's down there looking up at me but Sister Joan. 'Michael Kerr! I would have expected better of you.'

And me of her. Yes, we could have applied ourselves a bit more. We could have concentrated on the eschatological instead of the scatological. 'And he went into her and knew her . . .' Dick grins at Hilary. Hilary grins at Mary. Mary grins at me. Sister Joan looks up and reminds us that we're supposed to be in the sixth form, not the first.

But then she'd talk to us as if we *were* first formers. One day she'd come on like a passionate ecumenical, giving us a lengthy report (when she should have been attending to the curriculum) of some multi-faith conference she had attended. Next day she'd come sailing in, gather her cassock primly about her legs, and wave some new biblical commentary in the air. 'Boys and girls, listen . . . this is a very good book but, shhh, it's written by a Protestant.'

Dick laid into her over that. Why had she introduced the book in that way? Did she think it was funny? Because he didn't think it was funny at all. And that face of hers, normally as pale as her wimple, went very close to red.

After that, we had no sympathy for her at all when she had her crisis over *The Exorcist*. The priests were thundering against it from the pulpit, saying no Catholic should go anywhere near a cinema that was screening it. But she wanted to see it because she was 'intellectually curious' about exorcism. What should she do? When Dick told her she could go in disguise she got really shirty. 'Richard! I don't think you're taking this issue seriously.' She was right. But we all loved the idea of Sister Joan sneaking into an X-rated movie, and bringing down the wrath of the clergy on her head.

What was it they used to say about the Anchor…? With a Catholic church at the back and a Protestant one at the front, there was nowhere you could safely stagger without incurring the wrath of the clergy. Not that that ever did much to restrain the drinking. It still doesn't. The place is heaving every Friday and Saturday night. 'Aye, but it's not what it was in John Currid's day,' my Da says. 'It's full o' students.' But then there was no shortage of students around in John's last few years, as my Da would have noticed if he hadn't already taken his custom to the Sea Splash. I doubt if he's been in the Anchor more than twice since I started working weekends. Why should he bother? The Splash is nearly in his own back yard. He could have two drinks down him there in the time it would take him to stroll to the other end of the town.

But in another way he's right. The Anchor's not what it was. Larry Duffy's a decent enough boss, but he's not a family friend the way John Currid was. And there's nobody in the place now who's a patch on Martin. 'Best barman in Ireland,' my Da used to say, 'though I wish he'd get rid o' that scraggy oul' beard. It looks like the hairs came out, saw how far they had tae go, and went back in again.' He can talk: he's got a fair oul' chin himself, though my Ma's – which I've inherited – is even stronger.

Martin's is nothing like that. Anyway, it's done him no harm with the girlfriends. Until he started going out with Hilary he was a real flirt, chatting up every woman who set foot in the bar. They liked it too – even old biddies like Maisie thought he was God's gift to women. I wish I had half his confidence, half his charm.

I'm sure his brothers felt like that, too. Michael certainly did. I'd see him sometimes trying that trick of Martin's, flicking the ice cubes up in the air with the tongs and catching them behind his back in the glass. He caught about one in three, and the rest made puddles on the floor – just like they did when I tried it. But Martin could do it four times in a row without losing a single cube. He seemed to have more hands than the rest of us, as well as eyes in the back of his head. He'd be serving one customer, taking an order from another, shouting a greeting to a third who'd just come in the door behind him. He made me think of Franz Beckenbauer or Bobby Moore; one of those guys who always seemed to know what was going to happen next, one of the great sweepers.

John Currid didn't think I was one of those. He'd lean over the bar as I was brushing the floor, that purple bruise of a face resting on his fists. 'Michael, you're a pretty sweeper, but not a fast one,' he'd say. Well, I might have taken a bit longer than the rest of them, made a few more passes with the brush, but I also left fewer butts lying in the corners. I did more than my share of the sweeping and cleaning when I started, more than anybody else of that hand-numbing glass rinsing, too. It was my own fault; it wasn't as if the Currids were holding me back from serving. It was just that they were so good at it I was sure I'd make a balls of it.

I tell it differently, of course. Yeah, there's so much mystique about pulling a pint of Guinness in the Anchor that I was there for months before they'd let me do it...

The Anchor serves the best pint of stout in Portstewart, everybody used to say, as if it was any different there than in Murphy's or the Splash. It was coming off the same Guinness lorry, coming out of the same steel barrels, running through the same sort of plastic piping. How could it vary from place to place?

It *is* different in England, I'm sure, but only because they don't know how to serve it there. Everybody says they just pour it like a glass of water and slap it straight on the counter. They don't do what we do. Hold the glass at an angle of about sixty degrees to the tap. Put the tip of the tap in the glass and turn it on, partly open at first, then all the way. As it fills, bring the glass gradually to the vertical. Using a knife, skim off any bubbles into the drip tray. Then leave the pint to stand a couple of minutes, until that cloudy brown liquid has settled, until it's seven-eighths black and one-eighth creamy head. Then lift it again, put the nozzle of the tap in it, give it a final gentle squirt, and serve.

It's a doddle, really, so why did I used to be so scared of doing it? If I thought somebody was going to ask me to pull a pint I'd get the hell out from behind the bar and empty the ashtrays, or refill the ice bucket, or restock the shelves with bottled beer. Martin will serve you, I'd say, or John or Michael. Then Robert Thompson caught me that day when I was on my own, down behind the counter wiping the store-room dust off the bottles with a damp cloth. He leaned over the counter, those big bony shoulders like the points of a coat hanger in his jacket. 'So. There is a barman after all. A pint o' porter, son, quick as ye can.'

That was the first time I'd heard the word porter. I'd heard it clearly, too, and I knew I should know what it meant, but I *didn't* know. Me, the son of the man who drinks for Ireland, not knowing what porter was! How do I get out of this one? I know, I'll pretend I misheard him. I went to lift the port bottle.

'Naw, naw. Not port, son. *Porter*, Ah said.'

I looked at him, hoping he'd throw me a line.

But Robert was enjoying himself. The hangdog face was split by a big smile. 'Ye don't mean tae tell me, do ye, that ye don't know what porter is? Wait till I tell your oul' Da...'

He moved along the counter, slapped one of his goalkeeper's palms down on the Guinness tap. 'This is porter, son. Guinness, stout, porter – it's all the same. Now, ye're not goin' tae tell me that ye don't know how tae pull a pint, either...'

Too bloody right, I wasn't. Did he notice, I wonder, that my hand was shaking when I lifted the glass. But I tried to do it exactly the way I'd seen Martin do it so many times. I skimmed the bubbles, set it down, and stood watching as the brown went black and the head settled, as the magic worked for me, too.

'Are ye goin' tae just admire it, or are ye goin' tae hand it over?' Robert said. I gave it a final squirt and set it in front of him.

He took a deep slurp. 'Ah, it's a brev pint, son.' Then he put his money on the counter and moved off to a seat in the corner, shaking his head. 'Wait till Ah tell yer Da about the porter...'

He's a nice oul' boy, Robert, talks to anybody. He always passes the time of day with the soldiers when they come in. 'How ye doin',' he says, inclining his head at one of them, and the soldier proceeds to tell him that he's fine, thank you, and asks how Robert is. You'd think somebody would have briefed them: you'd think somebody would have told them that over here How ye doin' is like Hello. There's no question mark on the end of it; no need for any more of an answer than a nod. But they don't seem to have noticed that, just as they don't seem to have noticed how we order drinks.

They get dropped off their buses around the Strand Road or the Diamond, presumably having been told to disperse around the town. They wander into the pubs, a couple of them in Murphy's, two or three in the Anchor, another pair in the Sea Splash. The first thing you notice is the hair. They've obviously spent ages in front of the mirror combing it forward, trying to hide the born-leader forehead. If they strung lead shot to the fringe to hold it down it couldn't be more obvious. Some of them have been practising the accent, and they don't make a bad fist of it, but they still let themselves down when they come to order. 'Three pints of lager, please,' they say. Lager? Have they never listened to the locals? Don't they know that every man who lives round here orders beer by the name? It's Harp or Tennents or Carlsberg. It's never lager. So much for them trying to blend in...

Larry gets as twitchy about having them around as John did. He might look like he's only just got out of bed, but there's not much he misses. He wanders from room to room in the evening, nodding at the regulars, glancing under tables and chairs to make sure that no stranger has been in and left us a parcel. 'It's all right to drink in Portstewart,' the soldiers have been told. 'You'll be safe enough having a jar there.' But what about the rest of us? What if some lunatic takes it into his head to blow up the pub precisely because the squaddies think they're safe in it?

I did feel sorry for that guy in the Splash. There he was, sitting on a stool minding his own business, when that English woman came in and did everything but make a public announcement that he was a soldier. We all knew, of course. We'd clocked him as soon as he came in; a man off duty but on guard. We left him alone.

She wouldn't. She was trying to be friendly, I suppose, and took his reticence for shyness, burbling away in her party voice, trying to draw him out. 'You're English, aren't you? I thought I was the only one in the pub.'

'Yes, love.'

'Where are you from?'

'Manchester.'

'Really? My Dad's just moved there. Whereabouts?'

But as she drew up a stool next to him he was already

easing himself off his own stool, excusing himself to go to the loo. Next thing I knew he was flying past her and out through the door.

'He was a bit anti-social, wasn't he?' she said.

So I explained why.

'Oh. And I was sort of blowing his cover, wasn't I? You probably think I'm really stupid, don't you.'

And I did, at the time. But the more I've thought about it the more I've come to think that it wasn't so much stupidity as innocence; the sort of innocence I've never had. The muttering I've heard in this kitchen since the day I started to crawl has seen to that. Mind you, you can't afford to be innocent if you're living here. Look at that night I got off with Linda at Kelly's . . . if I hadn't had my wits about me then I'd have got my head kicked in.

Twenty-Three

If my Ma ever got to hear about that she'd say, 'Serves ye right for goin' tae Kelly's. Sure didn't I tell ye it was a hole?' And she did. It was comical how she tried to keep me away from the place when the girls had spent all their teenage weekends there. 'Drink, drugs and all the rest o' it. It's a real oul' den. Ah don't mind ye goin' out, but Ah don't want ye goin' anywhere near Kelly's. There's dancin' at the Northern Counties. What's wrong wi' goin' there?'

Well, for a start it's full of old maids and young farmers, the sort of people who think that Dr Hook is a GP. And the music! I've heard better from that geriatric Angus and His Organ in the Sea Splash. But we gave it a fair trial. We must have stayed at least two hours that first night before we walked on out to Kelly's. If I'd been drinking at that stage I'd probably have told my Ma we'd spent the whole night at the Counties, and I'd have been caught out. But because I was still on the orange juice and sober, I felt confident enough to tell her the truth. When she saw I'd survived without being knifed or turned into a junkie she was prepared to accept that Kelly's might have cleaned up its act. After that, there was nothing to stop us going straight there.

'Will that be enough?' my Ma says, pulling a fiver from the mug in the high cupboard and handing it over, and I never like to disabuse her. She can tell you how much dearer the flour is in Crazy Prices than in Stewarts', and whether that wardrobe in Gordon's will go under the hammer for fifty quid or sixty, but she hasn't a clue what it costs to go out for an evening. My Da's saved me from financial embarrassment a few times by catching me at the door and pressing another couple of quid into my hand. Whatever I say about him, he's always been decent in that way.

I used to feel the rest of them had been going to Kelly's for years before me, but it was probably only months. There was so much I seemed to have missed, so much that had happened when I wasn't there. But when you've heard the stories a few times you start to make them *your* stories. In one part of my head I know I was under the covers listening to Radio Caroline the night Thin Lizzy were playing, but in another part I know I was yards from the stage, close enough to see Phil Lynott, down on his knees, playing the guitar with his teeth. It was boiling in there that night, wasn't it?

But then it always was, it always is, in Kelly's. 'Northern Ireland's Hottest Nite Spot'. Well, it is for us, anyway. When we arrive we're immaculate – or some of us are.

We've spent the afternoon and most of our part-time earnings in Coleraine; the shirt's fresh off the rail from Clouds, the hair's still bouncy from Kim Britcher's blow-dry. We stand a while at the bar, eyeing up the talent, cool as fuck, until someone says, 'Will we go up now?' And two hours later we're back out in the freezing air, shirts sticking to our backs, hair plastered to our heads.

I know why we do it, but I don't know why we *keep* doing it. It's hardly the most efficient means to the end. You jerk about like a puppet during a few fast ones, in the hope that she's going to stick around for a slow one, but by that time you're sweating so much she doesn't want to come anywhere near you. *I* wouldn't want to come anywhere near me.

Sometimes you get lucky before you get sweaty. But not often. And what does the luck run to, and how long does it last? 'She was another one-night stand,' I tell the rest of them when we're comparing notes, but one-night cuddle would be more like it. A bit of French kissing, a hand fondling the boobs through the blouse until it meets the slightest resistance – that's as far as I've ever gone. Are the rest of the guys really at it like rabbits? Or are they just frustrated fumblers like me, asking themselves at the crucial moment, What if this girl was one of my sisters, and some guy was pawing her the way I'm doing now...?

Shirley's probably the only girl I've met at Kelly's that I've seen again in a different setting. Where was she from? Templepatrick? Somewhere like that. Miles away, anyway, unreachable if you haven't got a car, and as her old boy owns a racehorse she's probably used to being taken out by the sort of guy who has his own MG. And when I went to meet her in Portrush for our one and only proper date, I had to cadge a lift in Derek's.

'Portrush? Why d'ye wanna go tae Portrush, Michael? Ye're not meetin' a wee girl by any chance...? Is she good-lookin'?'

And she was. Slightly horsey herself, but beautiful horsey, not like Princess Anne. Long-faced, with huge brown eyes. I'd written that poem for her, but I didn't hand it over until we were going along the cliff walk. Barrys didn't seem the right place, and I was still feeling rough after the Cyclone. Taking her on the bumper cars was a mistake: it might have brought our legs close together, but it also seemed to give her the idea that I was fond of fairground rides. Knowing what the Cyclone did to my stomach last time, I should have said no when she started pulling me towards it, but I was scared she would think I was a wimp, or too tight to pay for a second ride, or both. So we climbed in, and the bar went down over our laps, and away we spun, first sideways and then somersaulting, Shirley screaming and laughing, me clamping my lips together. If I hadn't faked a coughing fit when she leaned over to kiss me, God knows what might have happened.

'You didn't really like that, did you?' she said when I staggered out, legs buckling like a foal's.

'Me? Yeah, it was great fun,' I told her.

But I did like the walk. I liked being able to talk to her without having a disco beat pounding up my legs and sweat trickling down my back. I liked knowing that she'd already decided to spend the whole afternoon with me and that I didn't have to jitterbug to win her attention. I liked feeling as though I had a girlfriend instead of a dance.

Considering we'd seen each other only twice before, in a disco so noisy we hardly talked, the poem was probably a bit over the top, but she seemed to like it.

'It's beautiful. Did you write it?'

'Yes.'

Which was true. It was in my handwriting. And quite a few of the lines were mine. It would have spoilt the moment to give a full co-writer credit to Smokey Robinson.

But that lie, that white lie, was the only one I told her. Otherwise I was completely straight. I did really fancy her, I did want to see her again, and I was heartsick that her holiday in Portrush was nearly over and that she lived so far away. I wanted her to stay. I wanted us to have a long loving relationship in which I would lose my virginity.

It wasn't like that last month with Linda. I just wanted to lose it, then and there, and she seemed keen enough to take it away.

'Hi, how ye doin',' she said, and I didn't recognize her at first, didn't remember we'd danced a few slow ones the week before. She pulled me on to the dance floor, in among her mates, guys and girls, all shouting and giggling at each other. 'Heaven Must Be Missing An Angel' faded into 'Sylvia's Mother', her mates disappeared, and she grabbed an arm and drew me against her. She took my hands and wrapped them round her back, then, as the song went on, gradually eased the right one down and on to her bum, her hand pressing on my hand, pressing herself into me. I knew she was pissed, that she wouldn't have been doing this if she hadn't had one hell of a lot of the crème de menthe I could taste on her breath when she kissed me. I felt horny and embarrassed at the same time. If we'd been on our own I'd have loved her taking charge, but there on the dance floor, with everybody looking on, I felt unmanned.

I thought she'd stop for breath when 'Sylvia's Mother' gave way to 'Sailing', but she didn't. She went on tonguing me, grinding against me. Then, just before the song ended, she said: 'D'ye wanna go outside?'

That's when I got my first proper look at her. As we stepped down from the dance floor one of the lights hit her full in the face, like a flashbulb going off. The frizzy blonde hair was definitely dyed; there were dark roots showing. Her face was pretty-going-plump. But she had a great body.

She pulled me through the crowd and the bouncers, out the front and round the corner. I started to make small talk – God knows why, because it wasn't what I wanted to do and she certainly wasn't interested. 'Kiss me,' she said, 'just kiss me.' She pushed me back against the wall, covered her lips with mine and drove her tongue in again. Then she started rubbing her hand up and down between my legs. The pebbledash was scoring lines on my back, but I didn't care. This, I thought, is it. We're going to do it. I'm going to do it.

And then I heard the shout. 'Orange or green, mate?'

She pulled her hand away, backed off me.

'Harry, what the fuck are you doin' here?' she said.

It was one of the guys she'd been with on the dance floor, a bruiser in black leather.

'Just makin' sure you're all right, Linda. And that *he's* all right.'

His face was in shadow, but I didn't need to see it to

know what sort of a look he was giving me.

''Course I'm all right,' she said. 'Now piss off and leave us alone.'

'Aye, but what about him?'

'He's fine. Leave 'im alone.'

'Aye, but is he orange, or is he green? Well, son? Ye got a tongue on ye − or has Linda chewed it off?''

He shoved his face into mine. I could smell the beer, see a gap between his two front teeth.

I made the calculation. Linda − that could be either Catholic or Protestant. And so could Harry. But in this area, knowing who's in the majority, you're not going to bellow questions about religion unless you're a Prod.

'Orange,' I said.

'See. Told ye,' said Linda.

I knew Harry wasn't convinced. But before he could say any more there was that other shout from up the hill.

'*Har−ry*! Quick!'

'You stay here,' he said. 'Ah'll be back in a minute.' And away he ran.

'Ye *are* orange, aren't ye?' said Linda, with a wink. 'Ye're not a wee Fenian in disguise?'

I didn't miss a beat, but somehow I still had time to hear the hymn in my head before I answered.

> *Faith of our fathers, holy faith,*
> *We will be true to Thee till death.*

'Me? I'm more Protestant than Ian Paisley,' I told her. And I gave her a few bars of 'The Sash' while I tried to figure out how the fuck I was going to get out of this one before Harry came back.

And then – God can't have been *that* pissed off – I looked round and there was Sean Hickey reversing out of a parking space. 'Mick. Wanna lift? Or are ye stayin' the night?'

So it was, ''Scuse me, Linda – friend o' mine – just gotta have a quick word,' an oh-so-casual walk to the car, and then we're gone, two green streaks in the dark.

Which is why I'll be going to London still a virgin. All bloody Loyalist fanatic Harry's fault. There we are, raring to go, when he turns up and demands to know whether Linda is about to be entered with a Protestant cock or a Catholic one.

I wonder would he allow a lapsed-Catholic one? Can you be lapsed if you still go to Mass every Sunday? I certainly feel I am. I'm there but not there. It washes over me but leaves me dry. I feel I'm in the presence of God maybe once a year, at Christmas midnight Mass when the choir is singing in Latin and I shut my eyes and hear angels. The rest of the time I wonder why I've bothered. Oh, all right, I'm keeping my Ma happy; but I could do that just as easily by strolling down the Prom, sitting for an hour over a coffee in Morelli's, and then going home to tell her that the chapel was packed and that Father McCamphill's looking more frail by the week. As it is, I might not be lying to her, but I'm lying to myself.

When we started reading *Portrait of the Artist*, I was shit-scared by that passage on eternity, the image of the bird flying to and from the mountain of sand with a grain at a time. But that was a year ago. What comes back to me time after time now is the exchange between Cranly and Stephen towards the end. If he's lost faith in the Catholic church, Cranly asks, does he intend to become a Protestant? No, Stephen says; he's not about to swap *a logical absurdity for an illogical one.*

My Ma's worried that that's what's going to happen to Anne and David's kids: that they'll be brought up as staunch wee Protestants. I don't know; I think they'll be a bit of both and harder to pigeonhole and that their own kids will have it easier as a result. Certainly easier than Anne and David, easier than Margaret and Graham.

I could hardly believe how much Margaret was telling me last week, especially as it was only the third time we'd seen each other since she left school, and that was a good two years ago. But we've always got on well, and I suppose she was desperate to talk and felt safe. She knows that while my family might be Catholic they're not rabid republicans like her own.

I could see she was in a state as soon as I arrived. 'Come round for a coffee,' she'd said, but when I turned up she looked at me as if I'd dropped in out of the blue. Even after we'd sat down, the slightest noise outside set her twitching. Some kid strolled past, kicked a stone at the garage, and she jumped as if the stone had hit her. Then when the YP Pools man knocked on the door she wouldn't get up to answer it and I had to do it.

'Come on,' I said, 'tell me what's the matter.'

She insisted nothing was wrong, but I could see that wasn't true. She looked hard at me, as if she was weighing me up. 'All right,' she said. 'Swear ye won't tell anybody this. It could be a matter o' life and death. Don't laugh – Ah know it sounds like somethin' out of a filim, but Ah'm serious.'

So I promised, and then she told me everything: how they'd got into debt after the wedding and couldn't possibly pay the bills out of Graham's wage packet, and so he'd become a reservist in the UDR. Now, on the nights when he was out on patrol, she was terrified of answering the door in case it was somebody with bad news – or worse.

She hadn't wanted him to do it, she'd said she'd go out and get a job, but he pointed out that nobody was likely to take her on when she was five-months pregnant. He'd talked her round. He knew a guy at work who did it and it was a doddle. The toughest part was the training sessions, when they had to run up and down those sand dunes on the Strand wearing full packs. And it wasn't as if they could be sent to Bandit Country; they did all their patrols in their own area. From the way she was telling me this, looking up at me every so often, anxious for me to nod in the right places, I could tell she was trying to convince herself all over again that he wasn't in any danger.

She wasn't succeeding. 'Soon as we get enough to pay off the table and chairs and the beds, that's it. He's talkin' about stayin' in and gettin' enough to kit out the baby's room. I've told him bugger the baby's room, I just want the baby to have a father.'

She's as scared of her own family as she is of any anonymous gunman. It was bad enough her marrying a Protestant, but if they get to know he's a Protestant helping the British Army they'll crucify her.

That must have been a hell of a scare Graham got the other night. There he is on patrol somewhere between Coleraine and Limavady. They stop a car and he's walking towards the driver's door when he recognizes the face: Margaret's Uncle Jim. So he pretends he's spotted something at the side of the road and walks over there, leaving some other guy to check the uncle's licence. 'He's ninety-nine per cent certain,' Margaret says, 'that Jim didn't see him.'

But what if he's wrong? Christ, it's no wonder the poor woman's scared to answer her own front door.

Rob from LA would like that story. It would sit neatly with the view he has of Northern Ireland. But I'd like to tell him another one just to muddy that view a wee bit.

Picture the scene, Rob. It's ten past midnight and I'm sitting with my Ma and Da and my brother Sean in the breakfast room, hugging the fire, half-watching the TV that's been on since the early evening Ulster News with its tally of bombings and shootings and hoaxes.

We hear the front door open and footsteps in the hall. The footsteps advance to the breakfast-room door and the jangly handle turns. The door sticks, as it always does, so whoever is behind it gives it a shove. We hear it judder, feel the draught on our backs. And then he's in among us, a big loose-limbed man in a black donkey jacket with the collar turned up. He's a Protestant, a Loyalist; in the dim light from the fire and the flickering screen we recognize his face, his beaky nose. He strides towards my Da, pulling something long and round from inside his jacket, and points it straight at him.

It's a bottle of whiskey.

Yes, it's New Year's Eve, Rob, and Tommy Nicholl has come to wish us, his Catholic neighbours, the compliments of the season.

Nobody's ever entirely at ease. Tommy effs and blinds now and again and my Ma hates that – though you'd think she'd be used to it after the way her brother talked. And you can see Tommy darting wee glances around for a while, as if he's worried he might be sitting under the Sacred Heart or some graven idol. But the point is that he comes in, that he comes first-footing here – to folk from the other side of the house.

I know that's not the way the script's meant to go. I know they'd never believe it in Hollywood. But that's the way it is – in Portstewart if not in Belfast or Derry.

I wonder where he is now, that wee boy who slept under the bed, that wee boy who brought the war with him into the back return . . . When I've got the wee front attic to myself I love lying in the dark listening to Radio Caroline, until those whistles and pops between ship and shore get so loud that they drown out the music. By that time I'm usually asleep, and the radio's bounced again on the floor and the battery's draining. But most nights, before I drift off, I hear that Barclay James Harvest song about the kids all over the world who are caught up in wars, with its two lines about this place:

> *I am a child of Northern Ireland,*
> *I am a small boy with blood on his hands.*

I think of that wee skitter in the back return, and wonder what's become of him and whose blood he might have on his hands.

I've avoided all that, avoided the schools for stone-throwers and rabble-rousers, and held fast to my Ma's maxim that there's good and bad on both sides. But maybe it'll be harder to do that when I reach the stage where I'm going job-hunting. That's assuming I come back at all. Look at the girls. There's none of them completely free of bitterness; they all feel they've had to leave Northern Ireland to get a fair chance.

'Are you running away?' that guy Simon said to me at the college. No, I'm not running away. I'm just growing up and I want to spread my wings. But I do want to fly where nobody will be asking whether I'm a Protestant bird or a Catholic one. And there's no avoiding that question here, however well we get on and however much we congratulate ourselves on living in a part of the country where the two sides are more likely to raise a glass to each other than a gun.

That's what my Da was doing in the Splash the other night: having a few glasses with the neighbours, doing a bit of fixing on my behalf. 'Ah'll sort somethin' out,' he said as he headed round the corner. 'Huh, Ah'm sure ye will,' my Ma muttered. But she was wrong this time. He did. All he had to say was that I needed to get to the airport on Tuesday, and that his car was on the blink, and next thing Mervyn had offered to run me there.

God knows what we'll talk about. It was Adrian who was my mate, never Mervyn. When was the last time we said much more than hello to each other? Must have been two years ago, when I bought all those eight-track tapes unheard and decided I didn't like Steely Dan and passed 'Can't Buy A Thrill' on to him. He told me I didn't know what I was missing – and shortly afterwards, of course, I discovered he was right.

Aside from that we've got nothing in common. I can't

wait to stop living in a boarding house and, according to my Ma, he wants to run one. She says he's thinking of taking over when Tommy and Mrs Nicholl knock it on the head. As if there wasn't irony enough in having him as my chauffeur... There I'll be, a Catholic making his escape from Ulster, but only after cadging a lift from a Protestant.